KU-246-473

# Contents

# Acknowledgements

We are grateful to the following for permission to reproduce
copyright material:
Laurence Pollinger Ltd and the Estate of the late Mrs Frieda
Lawrence Ravagli for the poems 'Revolution As Such', 'Robot
Feelings', 'Robot Democracy' and 'Property and No Property'
by D.H. Lawrence from *The Complete Poems of D.H. Lawrence*
published by William Heinemann Ltd and extracts from *The
Widowing of Mrs Holroyd* by D.H. Lawrence and *Collected Letters
of D.H. Lawrence* published by William Heinemann Ltd.

All other material by D.H. Lawrence in this volume was first
published during the writer's lifetime.

We are grateful to the following for supplying photographs:
Local Studies Library, Nottinghamshire County Library:
cover photographs, background and inserts, *above* (original
photograph owned by H F Gunns), *centre* (original photograph
owned by David Garnett), *below* (photograph by Nicholas
Murray); 87 (painting owned by Mrs Mary Wood); 131; 132
(original photograph owned by University of Nottingham
Library); 133; 134; 135 (photograph by Nottingham Castle
Museum); 137 (original photograph owned by Mr Cammack
and J H Haywood Ltd); 138 *left* (original photograph owned by
Nottingham University Library); 138 *right*; 139 *left* (original
photograph owned by Helen Corke); 139 *right*; 140 (original
photograph in Private Collection);
Nottingham University Library:
i (photograph by Witter Bynner); ii–iii; 136 (photograph by
Warren Roberts); 141 (original photograph owned by Francis
Gair Wilkinson).

# Introduction

David Herbert Lawrence was born in 1885, one of five children of a Nottinghamshire coal miner's family. When he died of tuberculosis in the south of France in 1930, he had long been established as one of the greatest English writers of the twentieth century.

Today, some of our major writers in England come from a working class background. A century ago even the bright and imaginative working class child had limited career opportunities. Bert Lawrence won a scholarship to a good grammar school in Nottingham, but, when he left, his first job was that of a junior clerk in a factory. The sudden death of Ernest, the second son in the family, followed quickly by Bert's serious illness, led to his leaving this job. After a slow recovery from pneumonia he did some teaching locally and then went on to train and qualify as a teacher. For most working class boys and girls with creative ability, a teaching career was then, in itself, a high achievement.

During Lawrence's teacher-training, however, he had started to write. Encouraged mainly by his first girl-friend, Jessie Chambers, a studious and sensitive farmer's daughter, he persevered with the writing of poems and stories. At the age of twenty four, when he was teaching in his first post at Croydon, Surrey, some of his poems were published in an influential London literary magazine. At twenty five his first novel was published and he was making a name for himself in the London literary world.

His home background inspired him to write one of the finest of all novels about working class life, *Sons and Lovers*, as well as a number of memorable short stories and plays about people in mining communities like the one in which he grew up. Yet, unlike some writers who have drawn major inspiration from their regional origins, Lawrence's writings are far from being predominantly regional in scope. His wide social connections provided material for an equally wide range of characterisations in his fiction. In 1912 his sensational elopement with Frieda, daughter of a German aristocrat and wife of a Nottingham

University professor, ripped him from his Nottinghamshire roots, and he became one of the most widely travelled of English writers. His travels inspired a rich variety of writing of all kinds.

The scope of Lawrence's work is not always appreciated, and the present Selection is designed to illustrate the wide range of experience reflected in his writings.

A writer's first inspirations often come from the environment in which he has grown up. *A Quarrel*, taken from Lawrence's autobiographical novel, *Sons and Lovers*, is a realistic and disturbing account of one of his parents' violent quarrels. In contrast, the short story entitled *Rex* describes with equal realism a true, happier occasion in the Lawrence children's lives when they tried to train a lively and defiant puppy. However, in a mining community tragedy can strike a family suddenly, and the impact of a husband's death in a pit accident is movingly displayed in *The Return of Holroyd*, the closing scene of Lawrence's play *The Widowing of Mrs Holroyd*. Families are seen in a happier setting in *The Wedding*, an episode taken from the novel *The Rainbow*. Here is a warm and sensitive account of the wedding of farmer Tom Brangwen's step-daughter, Anna. The comedy of the typical speeches and leg-pullings of relatives contrasts effectively with the more serious description of Brangwen's tender concern for his step-daughter and his thoughts of his own ageing – meditations which come so naturally to parents on a child's wedding-day.

*A Sequence of Love Poems* gives an insight into Lawrence's intense feelings for three women in his life – Jessie Chambers ("Miriam"), his mother, and Frieda. The tumult and the joy following Lawrence's elopement to Germany with Frieda, less than two years after the death of his mother whom he had worshipped, are revealed in *A Letter to Mrs Hopkin* which Lawrence wrote from Germany to a friend in Eastwood in 1912.

Lawrence responded readily to the atmosphere of places in which he stayed during his extensive travels from 1912 onwards. In Bavaria during 1913 he wrote *The Prussian Officer*. This is one of his finest short stories in which a Prussian officer's jealous and vindictive behaviour towards his orderly produces tensions which build up relentlessly to the violent climax of the story.

*A Sequence of Nature Poems* reveals another side to Lawrence, his sensitivity to nature. First developed in his love for the countryside close to his Nottinghamshire home, this sensitivity later inspired many poems recording his reactions to the plants and creatures encountered in the natural surroundings of Italy, Sicily, and New Mexico.

Lawrence responded with equal enthusiasm to seeing the people of countries he visited in their natural surroundings, and this enthusiasm produced vivid accounts of them in his travel books. His delight in becoming, for a time, a member of a local community, eating and talking with them, can be seen in *A Night at Mandas*, an entertaining account, taken from his travel book *Sea and Sardinia*, of an evening and night spent with the locals at a railway station restaurant and hotel at Mandas, in a remote part of Sardinia, during a tour of the island with Frieda in 1921. He wrote with equal enthusiasm in his private correspondence, as can be seen in *A Letter from Italy*.

*Samson and Delilah* is a short story set in Cornwall, where Lawrence lived for some time during the 1914–18 war. A stranger arrives at a remote inn and refuses to be turned out at closing time, claiming that the landlady is the wife he had left fifteen years previously. . . .

Towards the end of his life Lawrence wrote a large number of very short poems critical of modern society. Over half a century later many of these poems seem even more topical than when they were written. A brief selection is given in *A Handful of Thoughts*.

With *Death of a Gamekeeper*, an episode from the novel *The White Peacock*, the Selection returns to where it started – Lawrence's home area. This time, however, it is to the nearby countryside which inspired Lawrence's first writings. Here is a description of a young boy's terrified disbelief on finding his father's body in a quarry, and a description of the contrasting serenity of nature on the occasion of the gamekeeper's funeral at a country church. It reveals the strength of talent displayed in this, Lawrence's first novel.

To the last, his happy memories of the countryside and of his visits to the Haggs farm in the heart of it, yet only a fairly short walk from ugly Eastwood, remained. By way of an epilogue this Selection concludes with *A Letter to David Chambers*. This was written from France in 1928 to one of the farmer's sons from the Haggs farm, whom Lawrence remembered as "a thin little lad with very fair hair". The ending of the letter has the nostalgia of the exile: ". . . whatever else I am, I am somewhere still the same Bert who rushed with such joy to the Haggs."

# Rex

Since every family has its black sheep,[1] it almost follows that every man must have a sooty uncle. Lucky if he hasn't two. However, it is only with my mother's brother that we are concerned. She had loved him dearly when he was a little blond boy. When he grew up black, she was always vowing she would never speak to him again. Yet when he put in an appearance, after years of absence, she invariably received him in a festive mood, and was even flirty with him.

He rolled up one day in a dog-cart, when I was a small boy. He was large and bullet-headed and blustering, and this time, sporty. Sometimes he was rather literary, sometimes coloured with business. But this time he was in checks, and was sporty. We viewed him from a distance.

The upshot was, would we rear a pup for him. Now my mother detested animals about the house. She could not bear the mix-up of human with animal life. Yet she consented to bring up the pup.

My uncle had taken a large, vulgar public-house in a large and vulgar town. It came to pass that I must fetch the pup. Strange for me, a member of the Band of Hope,[2] to enter the big, noisy, smelly plate-glass and mahogany public-house. It was called The Good Omen. Strange to have my uncle towering over me in the passage, shouting "Hello, Johnny, what d'yer want?" He didn't know me. Strange to think he was my mother's brother, and that he had his bouts when he read Browning[3] aloud with emotion and éclat.

I was given tea in a narrow, uncomfortable sort of living-room, half kitchen. Curious that such a palatial pub should show such miserable private accommodations, but so it was. There was I, unhappy, and glad to escape with the soft fat pup. It was winter-time, and I wore a big-flapped black overcoat, half cloak. Under the cloak-sleeves I hid the puppy, who trembled. It was Saturday,

---

[1] "there is a black sheep in every flock" (proverb) – i.e. a member of the family who brings disgrace on it in some way

[2] an organisation whose members promised never to drink alcoholic liquor

[3] a then-popular Victorian poet

and the train was crowded, and he whimpered under my coat. I sat in mortal fear of being hauled out for travelling without a dog-ticket. However, we arrived, and my torments were for nothing.

The others were wildy excited over the puppy. He was small and fat and white, with a brown-and-black head: a fox terrier. My father said he had a lemon head – some such mysterious technical phraseology. It wasn't lemon at all, but coloured like a field bee. And he had a black spot at the root of his spine.

It was Saturday night – bath-night. He crawled on the hearth-rug like a fat white teacup, and licked the bare toes that had just been bathed.

"He ought to be called Spot," said one. But that was too ordinary. It was a great question, what to call him.

"Call him Rex – the King,"[1] said my mother, looking down on the fat, animated little teacup, who was chewing my sister's little toe and making her squeal with joy and tickles. We took the name in all seriousness.

"Rex – the King!" We thought it was just right. Not for years did I realize that it was a sarcasm on my mother's part. She must have wasted some twenty years or more of irony on our incurable naiveté.

It wasn't a successful name, really. Because my father and all the people in the street failed completely to pronounce the monosyllable Rex. They all said Rax. And it always distressed me. It always suggested to me seaweed, and rack-and-ruin. Poor Rex!

We loved him dearly. The first night we woke to hear him weeping and whinnying in loneliness at the foot of the stairs. When it could be borne no more, I slipped down for him, and he slept under the sheets.

"I won't have that little beast in the beds. Beds are not for dogs," declared my mother callously.

"He's as good as we are!" we cried, injured.

"Whether he is or not, he's not going in the beds."

I think now, my mother scorned us for our lack of pride. We were a little *infra dig*,[2] we children.

The second night, however, Rex wept the same and in the same way was comforted. The third night we heard our father

---

[1] the Latin word for king is "rex"

[2] shortened form of the Latin words *infra dignitatem*, meaning, here, "beneath her dignity"

plod downstairs, heard several slaps administered to the yelling, dismayed puppy, and heard the amiable, but to us heartless voice saying "Shut it then! Shut thy noise, 'st hear? Stop in thy basket, stop there!"

"It's a shame!" we shouted, in muffled rebellion, from the sheets.

"I'll give you shame, if you don't hold your noise and go to sleep," called our mother from her room. Whereupon we shed angry tears and went to sleep. But there was a tension.

"Such a houseful of idiots would make me detest the little beast, even if he was better than he is," said my mother.

But as a matter of fact, she did not detest Rexie at all. She only had to pretend to do so, to balance our adoration. And in truth, she did not care for close contact with animals. She was too fastidious. My father, however, would take on a real dog's voice, talking to the puppy: a funny, high, sing-song falsetto which he seemed to produce at the top of his head. "'S a pretty little dog!'s a pretty little doggy! – ay! – yes! – he is, yes! – Wag thy strunt,[1] then! Wag thy strunt, Rexie! – Ha-ha! Nay, tha munna – " This last as the puppy, wild with excitement at the strange falsetto voice, licked my father's nostrils and bit my father's nose with his sharp little teeth.

"'E makes blood come," said my father.

"Serves you right for being so silly with him," said my mother. It was odd to see her as she watched the man, my father, crouching and talking to the little dog and laughing strangely when the little creature bit his nose and toused[2] his beard. What does a woman think of her husband at such a moment?

My mother amused herself over the names we called him.

"He's an angel – he's a little butterfly – Rexie, my sweet!"

"Sweet! A dirty little object!" interpolated my mother. She and he had a feud from the first. Of course he chewed boots and worried our stockings and swallowed our garters. The moment we took off our stockings he would dart away with one, we after him. Then as he hung, growling vociferously, at one end of the stocking, we at the other, we would cry:

"Look at him, Mother! He'll make holes in it again." Whereupon my mother darted at him and spanked him sharply.

"Let go, sir, you destructive little fiend."

But he didn't let go. He began to growl with real rage, and

[1] dialect word meaning "tail"
[2] pulled roughly at, worried

3

hung on viciously. Mite as he was, he defied her with a manly fury. He did not hate her, nor she him. But they had one long battle with one another.

"I'll teach you, my Jockey![1] Do you think I'm going to spend my life darning after your destructive little teeth! I'll show you if I will!"

But Rexie only growled more viciously. They both became really angry, while we children expostulated earnestly with both. He would not let her take the stocking from him.

"You should tell him properly, Mother. He won't be driven," we said.

"I'll drive him farther than he bargains for. I'll drive him out of my sight for ever, that I will," declared my mother, truly angry. He would put her into a real temper, with his tiny, growling defiance.

"He's sweet! A Rexie, a little Rexie!"

"A filthy little nuisance! Don't think I'll put up with him."

And to tell the truth, he was dirty at first. How could he be otherwise, so young! But my mother hated him for it. And perhaps this was the real start of their hostility. For he lived in the house with us. He would wrinkle his nose and show his tiny dagger-teeth in fury when he was thwarted, and his growls of real battle-rage against my mother rejoiced us as much as they angered her. But at last she caught him *in flagrante*.[2] She pounced on him, rubbed his nose in the mess, and flung him out into the yard. He yelped with shame and disgust and indignation. I shall never forget the sight of him as he rolled over, then tried to turn his head away from the disgust of his own muzzle, shaking his little snout with a sort of horror, and trying to sneeze it off. My sister gave a yell of despair, and dashed out with a rag and a pan of water, weeping wildly. She sat in the middle of the yard with the befouled puppy, and shedding bitter tears she wiped him and washed him clean. Loudly she reproached my mother. "Look how much bigger you are than he is. It's a shame, it's a shame!"

"You ridiculous little lunatic, you've undone all the good it would do him, with your soft ways. Why is my life made a curse with animals! Haven't I enough as it is – "

There was a subdued tension afterwards. Rex was a little

[1] expression used for children or animals who were being naughty or mischievous: "You young Jockey!"
[2] in the act

white chasm between us and our parent.

He became clean. But then another tragedy loomed. He must be docked. His floating puppy-tail must be docked short. This time my father was the enemy. My mother agreed with us that it was an unnecessary cruelty. But my father was adamant. 'The dog'll look a fool all his life, if he's not docked.'' And there was no getting away from it. To add to the horror, poor Rex's tail must be *bitten* off. Why bitten? we asked aghast. We were assured that biting was the only way. A man would take the little tail and just nip it through with his teeth, at a certain joint. My father lifted his lips and bared his incisors, to suit the description. We shuddered. But we were in the hands of fate.

Rex was carried away, and a man called Rowbotham bit off the superfluity of his tail in the Nag's Head, for a quart of best and bitter.[1] We lamented our poor diminished puppy, but agreed to find him more manly and *comme il faut*.[2] We should always have been ashamed of his little whip of a tail, if it had not been shortened. My father said it had made a man of him.

Perhaps it had. For now his true nature came out. And his true nature, like so much else, was dual. First he was a fierce, canine little beast, a beast of rapine and blood. He longed to hunt, savagely. He lusted to set his teeth in his prey. It was no joke with him. The old canine Adam[3] stood first in him, the dog with fangs and glaring eyes. He flew at us when we annoyed him. He flew at all intruders, particularly the postman. He was almost a peril to the neighbourhood. But not quite. Because close second in his nature stood that fatal need to love, the *besoin d'aimer*[4] which at last makes an end of liberty. He had a terrible, terrible necessity to love, and this trammelled the native, savage hunting beast which he was. He was torn between two great impulses: the native impulse to hunt and kill, and the strange, secondary, supervening impulse to love and obey. If he had been left to my father and mother, he would have run wild and got himself shot. As it was, he loved us children with a fierce, joyous love. And we loved him.

When we came home from school we would see him standing at the end of the entry, cocking his head wistfully at the open

[1] a couple of pints of beer – probably a mixture of best mild and bitter
[2] as it should be (lit.), genteel
[3] "the old Adam" is a saying which refers to the basic badness in man's character. Rex has, thus, the basic doggy badness!
[4] need to love

country in front of him, and meditating whether to be off or not: a white, inquiring little figure, with green savage freedom in front of him. A cry from a far distance from one of us, and like a bullet he hurled himself down the road, in a mad game. Seeing him coming, my sister invariably turned and fled, shrieking with delighted terror. And he would leap straight up her back, and bite her and tear her clothes. But it was only an ecstasy of savage love, and she knew it. She didn't care if he tore her pinafores. But my mother did.

My mother was maddened by him. He was a little demon. At the least provocation, he flew. You had only to sweep the floor, and he bristled and sprang at the broom. Nor would he let go. With his scruff erect and his nostrils snorting rage, he would turn up the whites of his eyes at my mother, as she wrestled at the other end of the broom. "Leave go, sir, leave go!" She wrestled and stamped her foot, and he answered with horrid growls. In the end it was she who had to let go. Then she flew at him, and he flew at her. All the time we had him, he was within a hair's-breadth of savagely biting her. And she knew it. Yet he always kept sufficient self-control.

We children loved his temper. We would drag the bones from his mouth, and put him into such paroxysms of rage that he would twist his head right over and lay it on the ground upside-down, because he didn't know what to do with himself, the savage was so strong in him and he must fly at us. "He'll fly at your throat one of these days," said my father. Neither he nor my mother dared have touched Rex's bone. It was enough to see him bristle and roll the whites of his eyes when they came near. How near he must have been to driving his teeth right into us, cannot be told. He was a horried sight snarling and crouching at us. But we only laughed and rebuked him. And he would whimper in the sheer torment of his need to attack us.

He never did hurt us. He never hurt anybody, though the neighbourhood was terrified of him. But he took to hunting. To my mother's disgust, he would bring large dead bleeding rats and lay them on the hearth-rug, and she had to take them up on a shovel. For he would not remove them. Occasionally he brought a mangled rabbit, and sometimes, alas, fragmentary poultry. We were in terror of prosecution. Once he came home bloody and feathery and rather sheepish-looking. We cleaned him and questioned him and abused him. Next day we heard of six dead ducks. Thank heaven no one had seen him.

But he was disobedient. If he saw a hen he was off, and calling would not bring him back. He was worst of all with my father, who would take him walks on Sunday morning. My mother would not walk a yard with him. Once, walking with my father, he rushed off at some sheep in a field. My father yelled in vain. The dog was at the sheep, and meant business. My father crawled through the hedge, and was upon him in time. And now the man was in a paroxysm of rage. He dragged the little beast into the road and thrashed him with a walking stick.

"Do you know you're thrashing that dog unmercifully?" said a passerby.

"Ay, an' mean to," shouted my father.

The curious thing was that Rex did not respect my father any the more, for the beatings he had from him. He took much more heed of us children, always.

But he let us down also. One fatal Saturday he disappeared. We hunted and called, but no Rex. We were bathed, and it was bed-time, but we would not go to bed. Instead we sat in a row in our nightdresses on the sofa and wept without stopping. This drove our mother mad.

"Am I going to put up with it? Am I? And all for that hateful little beast of a dog! He shall go! If he's not gone now, he shall go."

Our father came in late, looking rather queer, with his hat over his eye. But in his staccato tippled fashion he tried to be consoling.

"Never mind, my duckie,[1] I s'll look for him in the morning."

Sunday came – oh, such a Sunday. We cried, and didn't eat. We scoured the land, and for the first time realized how empty and wide the earth is, when you're looking for something. My father walked for many miles – all in vain. Sunday dinner, with rhubarb pudding, I remember, and an atmosphere of abject misery that was unbearable.

"Never," said my mother, "never shall an animal set foot in this house again, while I live. I knew what it would be! I knew."

The day wore on, and it was the black gloom of bedtime, when we heard a scratch and an impudent little whine at the door. In trotted Rex, mud-black, disreputable, and impudent. His air of offhand "How d'ye do!" was indescribable. He trotted around with *suffisance*,[2] wagging his tail as if to say, "Yes, I've

[1] a term of endearment
[2] an air of self-conceit

7

come back. But I didn't need to. I can carry on remarkably well by myself." Then he walked to his water, and drank noisily and ostentatiously. It was rather a slap in the eye for us.

He disappeared once or twice in this fashion. We never knew where he went. And we began to feel that his heart was not so golden as we had imagined it.

But one fatal day reappeared my uncle and the dog-cart. He whistled to Rex, and Rex trotted up. But when he wanted to examine the lusty, sturdy dog, Rex became suddenly still, then sprang free. Quite jauntily he trotted round – but out of reach of my uncle. He leaped up, licking our faces, and trying to make us play.

"Why, what ha' you done wi' the dog – you've made a fool of him. He's softer than grease. You've ruined him. You've made a damned fool of him," shouted my uncle.

Rex was captured and hauled off to the dog-cart[1] and tied to the seat. He was in a frenzy. He yelped and shrieked and struggled, and was hit on the head, hard, with the butt-end of my uncle's whip, which only made him struggle more frantically. So we saw him driven away, our beloved Rex, frantically, madly fighting to get to us from the high dog-cart, and being knocked down, while we stood in the street in mute despair.

After which, black tears, and a little wound which is still alive in our hearts.

I saw Rex only once again, when I had to call just once at The Good Omen. He must have heard my voice, for he was upon me in the passage before I knew where I was. And in the instant I knew how he loved us. He really loved us. And in the same instant there was my uncle with a whip, beating and kicking him back, and Rex cowering, bristling, snarling.

My uncle swore many oaths, how we had ruined the dog for ever, made him vicious, spoiled him for showing purposes, and been altogether a pack of mard[2] soft fools not fit to be trusted with any dog but a gutter-mongrel.

Poor Rex! We heard his temper was incurably vicious, and he had to be shot.

And it was our fault. We had loved him too much, and he had loved us too much. We never had another pet.

It is a strange thing, love. Nothing but love has made the dog

[1] here, an open cart. Originally named when they actually had a box under the seat for sportsmen's dogs
[2] mard means spoilt or pampered

lose his wild freedom, to become the servant of man. And this very servility or completeness of love makes him a term of deepest contempt –' "You dog!"

We should not have loved Rex so much, and he should not have loved us. There should have been a measure. We tended, all of us, to overstep the limits of our own natures. He should have stayed outside human limits, we should have stayed outside canine limits. Nothing is more fatal than the disaster of too much love. My uncle was right, we had ruined the dog.

My uncle was a fool, for all that.

# A Quarrel

from the novel *Sons and Lovers*

At the wakes time[1] Morel was working badly, and Mrs Morel was trying to save against her confinement. So it galled her bitterly to think he should be out taking his pleasure and spending money, whilst she remained at home, harassed. There were two days' holiday. On the Tuesday morning Morel rose early. He was in good spirits. Quite early, before six o'clock, she heard him whistling away to himself downstairs. He had a pleasant way of whistling, lively and musical. He nearly always whistled hymns. He had been a choir-boy with a beautiful voice, and had taken solos in Southwell cathedral.[2] His morning whistling alone betrayed it.

His wife lay listening to him tinkering away in the garden, his whistling ringing out as he sawed and hammered away. It always gave her a sense of warmth and peace to hear him thus as she lay in bed, the children not yet awake, in the bright early morning, happy in his man's fashion.

At nine o'clock, while the children with bare legs and feet were sitting playing on the sofa, and the mother was washing up, he came in from his carpentry, his sleeves rolled up, his waistcoat hanging open. He was still a good-looking man, with black, wavy hair, and a large black moustache. His face was perhaps too much inflamed, and there was about him a look almost of peevishness. But now he was jolly. He went straight to the sink where his wife was washing up.

"What, are thee there!" he said boisterously. "Sluthe off an' let me wesh mysen."

"You may wait till I've finished," said his wife.

"Oh, mun I? An' what if I shonna?"

This good-humoured threat amused Mrs Morel.

"Then you can go and wash yourself in the soft-water tub."

"Ha! I can' an' a', tha mucky little 'ussy."[3]

---

[1] local holiday period (still called "Wakes Week" in parts of Northern England)

[2] Southwell is a small town in rural Nottinghamshire some 20 miles east-north-east of Eastwood

[3] a playful, rude form of address "'ussy" is a corruption of "housewife"

With which he stood watching her a moment, then went away to wait for her.

When he chose he could still make himself again a real gallant. Usually he preferred to go out with a scarf round his neck. Now, however, he made a toilet.[1] There seemed so much gusto in the way he puffed and swilled[2] as he washed himself, so much alacrity with which he hurried to the mirror in the kitchen, and, bending because it was too low for him, scrupulously parted his wet black hair, that it irritated Mrs Morel. He put on a turn-down collar, a black bow, and wore his Sunday tail-coat. As such, he looked spruce, and what his clothes would not do, his instinct for making the most of his good looks would.

At half-past nine Jerry Purdy came to call for his pal. Jerry was Morel's bosom friend, and Mrs Morel disliked him. He was a tall, thin man, with a rather foxy face, the kind of face that seems to lack eyelashes. He walked with a stiff, brittle dignity, as if his head were on a wooden spring. His nature was cold and shrewd. Generous where he intended to be generous, he seemed to be very fond of Morel, and more or less to take charge of him.

Mrs Morel hated him. She had known his wife, who had died of consumption, and who had, at the end, conceived such a violent dislike of her husband, that if he came into her room it caused her haemorrhage. None of which Jerry had seemed to mind. And now his eldest daughter, a girl of fifteen, kept a poor house for him and looked after the two younger children.

"A mean, wizzen[3] hearted stick!" Mrs Morel said of him.

"I've never known Jerry mean in *my* life," protested Morel. "A opener-handed and more freer chap you couldn't find anywhere, accordin' to my knowledge."

"Open-handed to you," retorted Mrs Morel. "But his fist is shut tight enough to his children, poor things."

"Poor things! And what for are they poor things, I should like to know."

But Mrs Morel would not be appeased on Jerry's score.

The subject of argument was seen, craning his thin neck over the scullery curtain. He caught Mrs Morel's eye.

"Mornin', missis! Mester[4] in?"

"Yes – he is."

[1] washed and tidied himself up
[2] rinsed
[3] withered or shrivelled (i.e. mean hearted)
[4] dialect, meaning Master (of the house)

Jerry entered unasked, and stood by the kitchen doorway. He was not invited to sit down, but stood there, coolly asserting the rights of men and husbands.

"A nice day," he said to Mrs. Morel.

"Yes."

"Grand out this morning – grand for a walk."

"Do you mean *you're* going for a walk?" she asked.

"Yes. We mean walkin' to Nottingham," he replied.

"H'm!"

The two men greeted each other, both glad: Jerry, however, full of assurance, Morel rather subdued, afraid to seem too jubilant in presence of his wife. But he laced his boots quickly, with spirit. They were going for a ten-mile walk across the fields to Nottingham. Climbing the hillside from the Bottoms,[1] they mounted gaily into the morning. At the Moon and Stars they had their first drink, then on to the Old Spot. Then a long five miles of drought to carry them into Bulwell[2] to a glorious pint of bitter. But they stayed in a field with some haymakers whose gallon bottle was full, so that, when they came in sight of the city, Morel was sleepy. The town spread upwards before them, smoking vaguely in the midday glare, fringing the crest away to the south with spires and factory bulks and chimneys. In the last field Morel lay down under an oak tree and slept soundly for over an hour. When he rose to go forward he felt queer.

The two had dinner in the Meadows, with Jerry's sister, then repaired to the Punch Bowl, where they mixed in the excitement of pigeon-racing. Morel never in his life played cards, considering them as having some occult, malevolent power – "the devil's pictures," he called them! But he was a master of skittles and of dominoes. He took a challenge from a Newark man, on skittles. All the men in the old, long bar took sides, betting either one way or the other. Morel took off his coat. Jerry held the hat containing the money. The men at the tables watched. Some stood with their mugs in their hands. Morel felt his big wooden ball carefully, then launched it. He played havoc among the nine-pins, and won half a crown, which restored him to solvency.

[1] the rows of miners' houses, referred to collectively as "the Bottoms" (built at the bottom of the hill)

[2] a village half way between Eastwood and Nottingham, a little way off the main route

By seven o'clock the two were in good condition. They caught the 7.30 train home.

In the afternoon the Bottoms was intolerable. Every inhabitant remaining was out of 'doors. The women, in twos and threes, bareheaded and in white aprons, gossiped in the alley between the blocks. Men, having a rest between drinks, sat on their heels and talked. The place smelled stale; the slate roofs glistered in the arid heat.

Mrs Morel took the little girl down to the brook in the meadows, which were not more than two hundred yards away. The water ran quickly over stones and broken pots. Mother and child leaned on the rail of the old sheep-bridge, watching. Up at the dipping-hole,[1] at the other end of the meadow, Mrs Morel could see the naked forms of boys flashing round the deep yellow water, or an occasional bright figure dart glittering over the blackish stagnant meadow. She knew William was at the dipping-hole, and it was the dread of her life lest he should get drowned. Annie played under the tall old hedge, picking up alder cones, that she called currants. The child required much attention, and the flies were teasing.

The children were put to bed at seven o'clock. Then she worked awhile.

When Walter Morel and Jerry arrived at Bestwood they felt a load off their minds; a railway journey no longer impended, so they could put the finishing touches to a glorious day. They entered the Nelson with the satisfaction of returned travellers.

The next day was a work-day, and the thought of it put a damper on the men's spirits. Most of them, moreover, had spent their money. Some were already rolling dismally home, to sleep in preparation for the morrow. Mrs Morel, listening to their mournful singing, went indoors. Nine o'clock passed, and ten, and still "the pair" had not returned. On a door-step somewhere a man was singing loudly, in a drawl: "Lead, kindly Light."[2] Mrs Morel was always indignant with the drunken men that they must sing that hymn when they got maudlin.

"As if 'Genevieve'[3] weren't good enough," she said.

The kitchen was full of the scent of boiled herbs and hops. On the hob a large black saucepan steamed slowly. Mrs Morel

[1] i.e. the pond once used for dipping the sheep
[2] a popular nineteenth century hymn
[3] i.e. "Sweet Genevieve", a sentimental song once particularly popular with drunken singers

took a panchion, a great bowl of thick red earth, streamed a heap of white sugar into the bottom, and then, straining herself to the weight, was pouring in the liquor.

Just then Morel came in. He had been very jolly in the Nelson, but coming home had grown irritable. He had not quite got over the feeling of irritability and pain, after having slept on the ground when he was so hot; and a bad conscience afflicted him as he neared the house. He did not know he was angry. But when the garden gate resisted his attempts to open it, he kicked it and broke the latch. He entered just as Mrs Morel was pouring the infusion of herbs out of the saucepan. Swaying slightly, he lurched against the table. The boiling liquor pitched. Mrs Morel started back.

"Good gracious," she cried, "coming home in his drunkenness!"

"Comin' home in his what?" he snarled, his hat over his eye.

Suddenly her blood rose in a jet.

"Say you're *not* drunk!" she flashed.

She had put down her saucepan, and was stirring the sugar into the beer. He dropped his two hands heavily on the table, and thrust his face forwards at her.

"'Say you're not drunk,'" he repeated. "Why, nobody but a nasty little bitch like you 'ud 'ave such a thought."

He thrust his face forward at her.

"There's money to bezzle[1] with, if there's money for nothing else."

"I've not spent a two-shillin' bit[2] this day," he said.

"You don't get as drunk as a lord on nothing," she replied. "And," she cried, flashing into sudden fury, "If you've been sponging on your beloved Jerry, why, let him look after his children, for they need it."

"It's a lie, it's a lie. Shut your face, woman."

They were now at battle-pitch. Each forgot everything save the hatred of the other and the battle between them. She was fiery and furious as he. They went on till he called her a liar.

"No," she cried, starting up, scarce able to breathe. "Don't call me that – you, the most despicable liar that ever walked in shoe-leather." She forced the last words out of suffocated lungs.

[1] to guzzle drink
[2] coin

14

"You're a liar!" he yelled, banging the table with his fist. "You're a liar, you're a liar."

She stiffened herself, with clenched fists.

"The house is filthy with you," she cried.

"Then get out on it – it's mine. Get out on it!" he shouted. "It's me as brings th' money whoam, not thee. It's my house, not thine. Then ger out on't – ger out on't!"

"And I would," she cried, suddenly shaken into tears of impotence. "Ah, wouldn't I, wouldn't I have gone long ago, but for those children. Ay, haven't I repented not going years ago, when I'd only the one" – suddenly drying into rage. "Do you think it's for *you* I stop – do you think I'd stop one minute for *you*?"

"Go, then," he shouted, beside himself. "Go!"

"No!" She faced round. "No," she cried loudly, "you shan't have it *all* your own way; you shan't do *all* you like. I've got those children to see to. My word," she laughed, "I should look well to leave them to you."

"Go," he cried thickly, lifting his fist. He was afraid of her. "Go!"

"I should be only too glad. I should laugh, laugh, my lord, if I could get away from you," she replied.

He came up to her, his red face, with its bloodshot eyes, thrust forward, and gripped her arms. She cried in fear of him, struggled to be free. Coming slightly to himself, panting, he pushed her roughly to the outer door, and thrust her forth, slotting the bolt behind her with a bang. Then he went back into the kitchen, dropped into his arm-chair, his head, bursting full of blood, sinking between his knees. Thus he dipped gradually into a stupor, from exhaustion and intoxication.

The moon was high and magnificent in the August night. Mrs Morel, seared with passion, shivered to find herself out there in a great white light, that fell cold on her, and gave a shock to her inflamed soul. She stood for a few moments helplessly staring at the glistening great rhubarb leaves near the door. Then she got the air into her breast. She walked down the garden path, trembling in every limb, while the child boiled within her. For a while she could not control her consciousness; mechanically she went over the last scene, then over it again, certain phrases, certain moments coming each time like a brand red-hot down on her soul; and each time she enacted again the past hour, each time the brand came down at the same points, till the mark was burnt in, and the pain burnt out, and at last she came to herself. She must have been half an hour in this delirious condition. Then the presence of the night came again to her. She glanced round in fear. She had wandered to the side garden, where she was walking up and down the path beside the currant bushes under the long wall. The garden was a narrow strip, bounded from the road, that cut transversely between the blocks, by a thick thorn hedge.

She hurried out of the side garden to the front, where she could stand as if in an immense gulf of white light, the moon streaming high in face of her, the moonlight standing up from the hills in front, and filling the valley where the Bottoms crouched, almost blindingly. There, panting and half weeping in reaction from the stress, she murmured to herself over and over again: "The nuisance! the nuisance!"

She became aware of something about her. With an effort she roused herself to see what it was that penetrated her consciousness. The tall white lilies were reeling in the moonlight, and the air was charged with their perfume, as with a presence. Mrs Morel gasped slightly in fear. She touched the big, pallid flowers on their petals, then shivered. They seemed to be stretching in the moonlight. She put her hand into one white bin: the gold scarcely showed on her fingers by moonlight. She bent down to look at the binful of yellow pollen; but it only appeared dusky. Then she drank a deep draught of the scent. It almost made her dizzy.

Mrs Morel leaned on the garden gate, looking out, and she lost herself awhile. She did not know what she thought. Except for a slight feeling of sickness, and her consciousness in the child, herself melted out like scent into the shiny, pale air. After a time the child, too, melted with her in the mixing-pot of moonlight, and she rested with the hills and lilies and houses, all swum together in a kind of swoon.

When she came to herself she was tired for sleep. Languidly she looked about her; the clumps of white phlox seemed like bushes spread with linen; a moth ricochetted over them, and right across the garden. Following it with her eye roused her. A few whiffs of the raw, strong scent of phlox invigorated her. She passed along the path, hesitating at the white rose-bush. It smelled sweet and simple. She touched the white ruffles of the roses. Their fresh scent and cool, soft leaves reminded her of the morning-time and sunshine. She was very fond of them.

But she was tired, and wanted to sleep. In the mysterious out-of-doors she felt forlorn.

There was no noise anywhere. Evidently the children had not been wakened, or had gone to sleep again. A train, three miles away, roared across the valley. The night was very large, and very strange, stretching its hoary distances infinitely. And out of the silver-grey fog of darkness came sounds vague and hoarse: a corncrake not far off, sound of a train like a sigh, and distant shouts of men.

Her quietened heart beginning to beat quickly again, she hurried down the side garden to the back of the house. Softly she lifted the latch; the door was still bolted, and hard against her. She rapped gently, waited, then rapped again. She must not rouse the children, nor the neighbours. He must be asleep, and he would not wake easily. Her heart began to burn to be indoors. She clung to the door-handle. Now it was cold; she would take a chill, and in her present condition!

Putting her apron over her head and her arms, she hurried again to the side garden, to the window of the kitchen. Leaning on the sill, she could just see, under the blind, her husband's arms spread out on the table, and his black head on the board. He was sleeping with his face lying on the table. Something in his attitude made her feel tired of things. The lamp was burning smokily; she could tell by the copper colour of the light. She tapped at the window more and more noisily. Almost it seemed as if the glass would break. Still he did not wake up.

After vain efforts, she began to shiver, partly from contact with the stone, and from exhaustion. Fearful always for the unborn child, she wondered what she could do for warmth. She went down to the coal-house, where there was an old hearth-rug she had carried out for the rag-man the day before. This she wrapped over her shoulders. It was warm, if grimy. Then she walked up and down the garden path, peeping every now and then under the blind, knocking, and telling herself that in the end the very strain of his position must wake him.

At last, after about an hour, she rapped long and low at the window. Gradually the sound penetrated to him. When, in despair, she had ceased to tap, she saw him stir, then lift his face blindly. The labouring of his heart hurt him into consciousness. She rapped imperatively at the window. He started awake. Instantly she saw his fists set and his eyes glare. He had not a grain of physical fear. If it had been twenty burglars, he would have gone blindly for them. He glared round, bewildered, but prepared to fight.

"Open the door, Walter," she said coldly.

His hands relaxed. It dawned on him what he had done. His head dropped, sullen and dogged. She saw him hurry to the door, heard the bolt chock. He tried the latch. It opened – and there stood the silver-grey night, fearful to him, after the tawny light of the lamp. He hurried back.

When Mrs Morel entered, she saw him almost running through the door to the stairs. He had ripped his collar off his neck in his haste to be gone ere she came in, and there it lay with bursten button-holes. It made her angry.

She warmed and soothed herself. In her weariness forgetting everything, she moved about at the little tasks that remained to be done, set his breakfast, rinsed his pit-bottle, put his pit-clothes on the hearth to warm, set his pit-boots beside them, put him out a clean scarf and snap-bag[1] and two apples, raked the fire, and went to bed. He was already dead asleep. His narrow black eyebrows were drawn up in a sort of peevish misery into his forehead while his cheeks' down-strokes, and his sulky mouth, seemed to be saying: "I don't care who you are nor what you are, I *shall* have my own way."

Mrs Morel knew him too well to look at him. As she unfastened her brooch at the mirror, she smiled faintly to see her face all smeared with the yellow dust of lilies. She brushed it off, and at last lay down. For some time her mind continued snapping and jetting sparks, but she was asleep before her husband awoke from the first sleep of his drunkenness.

# The Return of Holroyd

*This episode consists of the final minutes of the play* The Widowing of Mrs Holroyd. *It is evening at the small miner's cottage which is the home of the Holroyd family. Holroyd, a pleasure-loving miner who often returns home at night drunk and violent, hasn't returned home from work. He hasn't been seen in the local pubs this evening, however, and Mrs Holroyd and her mother-in-law, who has just joined her, are now worried that he may have had an accident.*

*There is a knock at the door,* MRS HOLROYD *opens.*

RIGLEY: They tell me, missus, as your mester's not hoom yet.

MRS HOLROYD: No – who is it?

GRANDMOTHER: Ask him to step inside. Don't stan' there lettin' the fog in.

    RIGLEY *steps in. He is a tall, bony, very roughly hewn collier.*

RIGLEY: Good evenin'.

GRANDMOTHER: Oh, is it you, Mr Rigley? (*In a querulous, spiteful tone to* MRS HOLROYD.) He butties[1] along with Charlie.

MRS HOLROYD: Oh!

RIGLEY: An' han yer seen nowt on 'im?

MRS HOLROYD: No – was he all right at work?

RIGLEY: Well, e' wor nowt to mention. A bit short, like: 'adna much to say, I canna ma'e out what 'e's done wi' 'issen. (*He is manifestly uneasy, does not look at the two women.*)

GRANDMOTHER: An' did 'c come up i' th' same bantle[2] wi' you?

RIGLEY: No – 'e didna. As Ah was comin' out o' th' stall, Ah shouted, "Art comin', Charlie? Wc're a' off." An' 'e said, "Ah'm comin' in a minute." 'E wor just finishin' a stint, like, an' 'e wanted ter get it set. An' 'e 'd been a bit roughish in 'is temper, like, so I thöwt 'e didna want ter walk to th' bottom[3] wi' us. . . .

GRANDMOTHER (*wailing*): An' what's 'e gone an' done to himself?

---

[1] the two men who work together at the coal face are known as "butties"

[2] the group of men returning in the cage from the coal face at the end of their shift

[3] bottom of the pit shaft – i.e. where the cage was waiting

RIGLEY: Nay, missis, yo munna ax me that. 'E's non done owt as ah know on. On'y I wor thinkin', 'appen summat 'ad 'appened to 'im, like, seein' as nob'dy had any knowings of 'im comin' up.

MRS HOLROYD: What is the matter, Mr Rigley? Tell us it out.

RIGLEY: I canna do that, missis. It seems as if 'e niver come up th' pit – as far as we can make out. 'Appen a bit o' stuff's fell an' pinned 'im.

GRANDMOTHER (*wailing*): An' 'ave you left 'im lying down there in the pit, poor thing?

RIGLEY (*uneasily*): I couldna say for certain where 'e is.

MRS HOLROYD (*agitated*): Oh, it's very likely not very bad, mother! Don't let us run to meet trouble.

RIGLEY: We 'ave to 'ope for th' best, missis, all on us.

GRANDMOTHER (*wailing*): Eh, they'll bring 'im 'ome, I know they will, smashed up an' broke! An' one of my sons they've burned down pit till the flesh dropped off 'im, an' one was shot till 'is shoulder was all of a mosh,[1] an' they brought 'em 'ome to me. An' now there's this. . . .

MRS HOLROYD (*shuddering*): Oh, don't, mother. (*Appealing to* RIGLEY.) You don't know that he's hurt?

RIGLEY (*shaking his head*): I canna tell you.

MRS HOLROYD (*in a high hysterical voice*): Then what is it?

RIGLEY (*very uneasy*): I canna tell you. But yon young electrician – Mr Blackmore – 'e rung down to the night deputy, an' it seems as though there's been a fall or summat. . . .

GRANDMOTHER: Eh, Lizzie, you parted from him in anger. You little knowed how you'd meet him again.

RIGLEY (*making an effort*): Well, I'd 'appen best be goin' to see what's betide.[2]

*He goes out.*

GRANDMOTHER: I'm sure I've had my share of bad luck, I have. I'm sure I've brought up five lads in the pit, through accidents and troubles, and now there's this. The Lord has treated me very hard, very hard. It's a blessing, Lizzie, as you've got a bit of money, else what would 'ave become of the children?

MRS HOLROYD: Well, if he's badly hurt, there'll be the Union-pay, and sick-pay – we shall manage. And perhaps it's *not* very much.

[1] mash
[2] happened

GRANDMOTHER : There's no knowin' but what they'll be carryin' him to die 'i th' hospital.

MRS HOLROYD : Oh, don't say so, mother – it won't be so bad, you'll see.

GRANDMOTHER : How much money have you, Lizzie, comin'?

MRS HOLROYD : I don't know – not much over a hundred pounds.

GRANDMOTHER *(shaking her head)* : An' what's that, what's that?

MRS HOLROYD *(sharply)* : Hush!

GRANDMOTHER *(crying)* : Why, what?

> MRS HOLROYD *opens the door. In the silence can be heard the pulsing of the fan engine, then the driving engine chuffs rapidly : there is a skirr of brakes on the rope as it descends.*

MRS HOLROYD : That's twice they've sent the chair down – I wish we could see. . . . Hark!

GRANDMOTHER : What is it?

MRS HOLROYD : Yes – it's stopped at the gate. It's the doctor's.

GRANDMOTHER *(coming to the door)* : What, Lizzie?

MRS HOLROYD : The doctor's motor. *(She listens acutely.)* Dare you stop here, mother, while I run up to the top an' see?

GRANDMOTHER : You'd better not go, Lizzie, you'd better not. A woman's best away.

MRS HOLROYD : It is unbearable to wait.

GRANDMOTHER : Come in an' shut the door – it's a cold that gets in your bones.

> MRS HOLROYD *goes in.*

MRS HOLROYD : Perhaps while he's in bed we shall have time to change him. It's an ill wind brings no good. He'll happen be a better man.

GRANDMOTHER : Well, you can but try. Many a woman's thought the same.

MRS HOLROYD : Oh, dear, I wish somebody would come. He's never been hurt since we were married.

GRANDMOTHER : No, he's never had a bad accident, all the years he's been in the pit. He's been luckier than most. But everybody has it, sooner or later.

MRS HOLROYD *(shivering)* : It *is* a horrid night.

GRANDMOTHER *(querulous)* : Yes, come your ways in.

MRS HOLROYD : Hark!

> *There is a quick sound of footsteps.* BLACKMORE *comes into the light of the doorway.*

BLACKMORE : They're bringing him.

MRS HOLROYD (*quickly putting her hand over her breast*): What is it?

BLACKMORE: You can't tell anything's the matter with him – it's not marked him at all.

MRS HOLROYD: Oh, what a blessing! And is it much?

BLACKMORE: Well——

MRS HOLROYD: What is it?

BLACKMORE: It's the worst.

GRANDMOTHER: Who is it? – What does he say?

> MRS HOLROYD *sinks on the nearest chair with a horrified expression.* BLACKMORE *pulls himself together and enters the room. He is very pale.*

BLACKMORE: I came to tell you they're bringing him home.

GRANDMOTHER: And you said it wasn't very bad, did you?

BLACKMORE: No – I said it was – as bad as it could be.

MRS HOLROYD (*rising and crossing to her* MOTHER-IN-LAW, *flings her arms round her; in a high voice*): Oh, mother, what shall we do? What shall we do?

GRANDMOTHER: You don't mean to say he's dead?

BLACKMORE: Yes.

GRANDMOTHER (*staring*): God help us, and how was it?

BLACKMORE: Some stuff fell.

GRANDMOTHER (*rocking herself and her daughter-in-law – both weeping*): Oh, God have mercy on us! Oh, God have mercy on us! Some stuff fell on him. An' he'd not even time to cry for mercy; oh, God spare him! Oh, what shall we do for comfort? To be taken straight out of his sins.[1] Oh, Lizzie, to think he should be cut off in his wickedness. He's been a bad lad of late, he has, poor lamb. He's gone very wrong of late years, poor dear lamb, very wrong. Oh, Lizzie, think what's become of him now! If only you'd tried to be different with him.

MRS HOLROYD (*moaning*): Don't, mother, don't. I can't bear it.

BLACKMORE (*cold and clear*): Where will you have him laid? The men will be here in a moment.

MRS HOLROYD (*staring up*): They can carry him up to bed——

BLACKMORE: It's no good taking him upstairs. You'll have to wash him and lay him out.

MRS HOLROYD (*startled*): Well——

BLACKMORE: He's in his pit-dirt.

---

[1] a very old religious belief that sudden death prevented the vital act of a dying person's praying for forgiveness of sins on earth and repenting for his sins

GRANDMOTHER: He is, bless him. We'd better have him down here, Lizzie, where we can handle him.

MRS HOLROYD: Yes.

*She begins to put the tea things away, but drops the sugar out of the basin and the lumps fly broadcast.*

BLACKMORE: Never mind, I'll pick those up. You put the children's clothes away.

MRS HOLROYD *stares witless around. The* GRANDMOTHER *sits rocking herself and weeping.* BLACKMORE *clears the table, putting the pots in the scullery. He folds the white tablecloth and pulls back the table. The door opens,* MRS HOLROYD *utters a cry.* RIGLEY *enters.*

RIGLEY: They're bringing him now, missis.

MRS HOLROYD: Oh!

RIGLEY (*simply*): There must ha' been a fall directly after we left him.

MRS HOLROYD (*frowning, horrified*): No – no!

RIGLEY (*to* BLACKMORE): It fell a' back of him, an' shut 'im in as you might shut a loaf 'i th' oven. It never touched him.

MRS HOLROYD (*staring distractedly*): Well, then——

RIGLEY: You see, it come on 'im as close as a trap on a mouse, an' gen him no air, an' what wi' th' gas, it smothered him. An' it wouldna be so very long about it neither.

MRS HOLROYD (*quiet with horror*): Oh!

GRANDMOTHER: Eh, dear – dear. Eh, dear – dear.

RIGLEY (*looking hard at her*): I wasna to know what 'ud happen.

GRANDMOTHER (*not heeding him but weeping all the time*): But the Lord gave him time to repent. He'd have a few minutes to repent. Ay, I hope he did, I hope he did, else what was to become of him. The Lord cut him off in his sins, but He gave him time to repent.

RIGLEY *looks away at the wall.* BLACKMORE *has made a space in the middle of the floor.*

BLACKMORE: If you'll take the rocking-chair off the end of the rug, Mrs Holroyd, I can pull it back a bit from the fire, and we can lay him on that.

GRANDMOTHER (*petulantly*): What's the good of messing about —— (*She moves.*)

MRS HOLROYD: It suffocated him?

RIGLEY (*shaking his head, briefly*): Yes. 'Appened th' afterdamp[1]

---

[1] carbon dioxide gas which suffocates

BLACKMORE: He'd be dead in a few minutes.

MRS HOLROYD: No – oh, think!

BLACKMORE: You mustn't think.

RIGLEY (*suddenly*): They commin'!

> MRS HOLROYD *stands at bay. The* GRANDMOTHER *half rises.* RIGLEY *and* BLACKMORE *efface themselves as much as possible. A man backs into the room, bearing the feet of the dead man, which are shod in great pit boots. As the head bearer comes awkwardly past the table, the coat with which the body is covered slips off, revealing* HOLROYD *in his pit-dirt, naked to the waist.*

MANAGER (*a little stout, white-bearded man*): Mind now, mind. Ay, missis, what a job, indeed, it is! (*Sharply.*) Where mun they put him?

MRS HOLROYD (*turning her face aside from the corpse*): Lay him on the rug.

MANAGER: Steady now, do it steady.

SECOND BEARER (*rising and pressing back his shoulders*): By Guy,[1] but 'e 'ings heavy.

MANAGER: Yi, Joe, I'll back my life o' that.

GRANDMOTHER: Eh, Mr Chambers, what's this affliction on my old age. You kept your sons out o' the pit, but all mine's in. And to think of the trouble I've had – to think o' the trouble that's come out of Brinsley pit to me.

MANAGER: It has that, it 'as that, missis. You seem to have had more'n your share; I'll admit it, you have.

MRS HOLROYD (*who has been staring at the men*): It is too much!

> BLACKMORE *frowns;* RIGLEY *glowers at her.*

MANAGER: You never knowed such a thing in your life. Here's a man, holin' a stint,[2] just finishin', (*He puts himself as if in the holer's position, gesticulating freely.*) an' a lot o' stuff falls behind him, clean as a whistle, shuts him up safe as a worm in a nut and niver touches him – niver knowed such a thing in your life.

MRS HOLROYD: Ugh!

MANAGER: It niver hurt him – niver touched him.

MRS HOLROYD: Yes, but – but how long would he *be* (*She makes a sweeping gesture; the* MANAGER *looks at her and will not help her out.*) – how long would it take – ah – to – to kill him?

MANAGER: Nay, I canna tell ye. 'E didna seem to ha' strived

---

[1] probably a variation of "my guyney" – dialect for "my word"

[2] mining term meaning to cut a passageway or to cut round a block of coal

much to get out – did he, Joe?

SECOND BEARER: No, not as far as Ah'n seen.

FIRST BEARER: You look at 'is 'ands, you'll see then. 'E'd non ha'e room to swing the pick.

*The* MANAGER *goes on his knees.*

MRS HOLROYD (*shuddering*): Oh, don't!

MANAGER: Ay, th' nails is broken a bit——

MRS HOLROYD (*clenching her fists*): Don't!

MANAGER: 'E'd be sure ter ma'e a bit of a fight. But th' gas 'ud soon get hold on 'im. Ay, it's an awful thing to think of, it is indeed.

MRS HOLROYD (*her voice breaking*): I can't bear it!

MANAGER: Eh, dear, we none on us know what's comin' next.

MRS HOLROYD (*getting hysterical*): Oh, it's too awful, it's too awful!

BLACKMORE: You'll disturb the children.

GRANDMOTHER: And you don't want *them* down here.

MANAGER: 'E'd no business to ha' been left, you know.

RIGLEY: An' what man, dost think, wor goin' to sit him down on his hams[1] an' wait for a chap as wouldna say "thank yer" for his cump'ny? 'E'd bin ready to fall out wi' a flicker o' the candle, so who dost think wor goin' ter stop when we knowed e' on'y kep on so's to get shut on us.

MANAGER: Tha'rt quite right, Bill, quite right. But theer you are.

RIGLEY: An' if we'd stopped, what good would it ha' done——

MANAGER: No, 'appen not, 'appen not.

RIGLEY: For, not known——

MANAGER: I'm sayin' nowt agen thee, neither one road nor t'other. (*There is a general silence – then, to* MRS HOLROYD.) I should think th' inquest'll be at th' New Inn to-morrow, missis. I'll let you know.

MRS HOLROYD: Will there have to be an inquest?

MANAGER: Yes – there'll have to be an inquest. Shall you want anybody in, to stop with you to-night?

MRS HOLROYD: No.

MANAGER: Well, then, we'd best be goin'. I'll send my missis down first thing in the morning. It's a bad job, a bad job, it is. You'll be a' right then?

MRS HOLROYD: Yes.

---

[1] bottom (hams = buttocks)

MANAGER: Well, good night then – good night all.

ALL: Good night. Good night.

*The* MANAGER, *followed by the two bearers, goes out, closing the door.*

RIGLEY: It's like this, missis. I never should ha' gone, if he hadn't wanted us to.

MRS HOLROYD: Yes, I know.

RIGLEY: 'E wanted to come up by 's sen.

MRS HOLROYD (*wearily*): I know how it was, Mr Rigley.

RIGLEY: Yes——

BLACKMORE: Nobody could foresee.

RIGLEY (*shaking his head*): No. If there's owt, missis, as you want——

MRS HOLROYD: Yes – I think there isn't anything.

RIGLEY (*after a moment*): Well – good night – we've worked i' the same stall[1] ower four years now——

MRS HOLROYD: Yes.

RIGLEY: Well, good night, missis.

MRS HOLROYD AND BLACKMORE: Good night.

*The* GRANDMOTHER *all this time has been rocking herself to and fro, moaning and murmuring beside the dead man. When* RIGLEY *has gone* MRS HOLROYD *stands staring distractedly before her. She has not yet looked at her husband.*

GRANDMOTHER: Have you got the things ready, Lizzie?

MRS HOLROYD: What things?

GRANDMOTHER: To lay the child out.

MRS HOLROYD (*she shudders*): No – what?

GRANDMOTHER: Haven't you put him by a pair o' white stockings, nor a white shirt?

MRS HOLROYD: He's got a white cricketing shirt – but not white stockings.

GRANDMOTHER: Then he'll have to have his father's. Let me look at the shirt, Lizzie. (MRS HOLROYD *takes one from the dresser drawer.*) This'll never do – a cold, canvas thing wi' a turndown collar. I s'll 'ave to fetch his father's. (*Suddenly.*) You don't want no other woman to touch him, to wash him and lay him out, do you?

MRS HOLROYD (*weeping*): No.

GRANDMOTHER: Then I'll fetch him his father's gear. We

[1] the section of coal face worked exclusively by the two "butties" Holroyd and Rigley

mustn't let him set, he'll be that heavy, bless him. (*She takes her shawl.*) I shan't be more than a few minutes, an' the young fellow can stop here till I come back.

BLACKMORE: Can't I go for you, Mrs Holroyd?

GRANDMOTHER: No. *You* couldn't find the things. We'll wash him as soon as I get back, Lizzie.

MRS HOLROYD: All right.

> She watches her mother-in-law go out. Then she starts, goes in the scullery for a bowl, in which she pours warm water. She takes a flannel and soap and towel. She stands, afraid to go any further.

BLACKMORE: Well!

MRS HOLROYD: This is a judgment on us.[1]

BLACKMORE: Why?

MRS HOLROYD: On me, it is——

BLACKMORE: How?

MRS HOLROYD: It is.

> BLACKMORE *shakes his head.*

MRS HOLROYD: Yesterday, you talked of murdering him.

BLACKMORE: Well!

MRS HOLROYD: Now we've done it.

BLACKMORE: How?

MRS HOLROYD: He'd have come up with the others, if he hadn't felt – felt me murdering him.

BLACKMORE: But we can't help it.

MRS HOLROYD: It's my fault.

BLACKMORE: Don't be like that!

MRS HOLROYD (*looking at him – then indicating her husband*): I daren't see him.

BLACKMORE: No?

MRS HOLROYD: I've killed him, that is all.

BLACKMORE: No, you haven't.

MRS HOLROYD: Yes, I have.

BLACKMORE: *We* couldn't help it.

MRS HOLROYD: If he hadn't felt, if he hadn't *known*, he wouldn't have stayed, he'd have come up with the rest.

BLACKMORE: Well, and even if it was so, we can't help it now.

MRS HOLROYD: But we've killed him.

BLACKMORE: Ah, I'm tired——

MRS HOLROYD: Yes.

---

[1] Blackmore had asked Mrs Holroyd to leave her husband and to go away with him

BLACKMORE (*after a pause*): Shall I stay?

MRS HOLROYD: I – I daren't be alone with him.

BLACKMORE (*sitting down*): No.

MRS HOLROYD: I don't love him. Now he's dead. I don't love him. He lies like he did yesterday.[1]

BLACKMORE: I suppose, being dead – I don't know——

MRS HOLROYD: I think you'd better go.

BLACKMORE (*rising*): Tell me.

MRS HOLROYD: Yes.

BLACKMORE: You want me to go.

MRS HOLROYD: No – but *do* go. (*They look at each other.*)

BLACKMORE: I shall come to-morrow.

> BLACKMORE *goes out.*

> MRS HOLROYD *stands very stiff, as if afraid of the dead man. Then she stoops down and begins to sponge his face, talking to him.*

MRS HOLROYD: My dear, my dear – oh, my dear! I can't bear it, my dear – you shouldn't have done it. You shouldn't have done it. Oh – I can't bear it, for you. Why couldn't I do anything for you? The children's father – my dear – I wasn't good to you. But you shouldn't have done this to me. Oh, dear, oh, dear! Did it hurt you! – oh, my dear, it hurt you – oh, I can't bear it. No, things aren't fair – we went wrong, my dear. I never loved you enough – I never did. What a shame for you! It was a shame. But you didn't – you didn't try. I *would* have loved you – I tried hard. What a shame for you! It was so cruel for you. You couldn't help it – my dear, my dear. You couldn't help it. And I can't do anything for you, and it hurt you so! (*She weeps bitterly, so her tears fall on the dead man's face; suddenly she kisses him.*) My dear, my dear, what can I do for you, what can I? (*She weeps as she wipes his face gently.*)

> *Enter* GRANDMOTHER.

GRANDMOTHER (*putting a bundle on the table, and taking off her shawl*): You're not all by yourself?

MRS HOLROYD: Yes.

GRANDMOTHER: It's a wonder you're not frightened. You've not washed his face.

MRS HOLROYD: Why should I be afraid of him – now, mother?

GRANDMOTHER (*weeping*): Ay, poor lamb, I can't think as ever

---

[1] i.e. when he had collapsed to the ground in a stupor after coming home drunk and violent and fighting with Blackmore

you could have had reason to be frightened of him, Lizzie.

MRS HOLROYD: Yes – once——

GRANDMOTHER: Oh, but he went wrong. An' he was a taking[1] lad, as iver was. (*She cries pitifully.*) And when I waked his father up and told him, he sat up in bed staring over his whiskers, and said should he come up? But when I'd managed to find the shirt and things, he was still in bed. You don't known what it is to live with a man that has no feeling. But you've washed him, Lizzie?

MRS HOLROYD: I was finishing his head.

GRANDMOTHER: Let me do it, child.

MRS HOLROYD: I'll finish that.

GRANDMOTHER: Poor lamb – poor dear lamb! Yet I wouldn't wish him back, Lizzie. He must ha' died peaceful, Lizzie. He seems to be smiling. He always had such a rare smile on him – not that he's smiled much of late——

MRS HOLROYD: I loved him for that.

GRANDMOTHER: Ay, my poor child – my poor child.

MRS HOLROYD: He looks nice, mother.

GRANDMOTHER: I hope he made his peace with the Lord.

MRS HOLROYD: Yes.

GRANDMOTHER: If he hadn't time to make his peace with the Lord, I've no hopes of him. Dear o' me, dear o' me. Is there another bit of flannel anywhere?

MRS HOLROYD *rises and brings a piece. The* GRANDMOTHER *begins to wash the breast of the dead man.*

GRANDMOTHER: Well, I hope you'll be true to his children at least, Lizzie. (MRS HOLROYD *weeps – the old woman continues her washing.*) Eh – and he's fair as a lily. Did you ever see a man with a whiter skin – and flesh as fine as the driven snow. He's beautiful, he is, the lamb. Many's the time I've looked at him, and I've felt proud of him, I have. And now he lies here. And such arms on 'im! Look at the vaccination marks, Lizzie. When I took him to be vaccinated, he had a little pink bonnet with a feather. (*Weeps.*) Don't cry, my girl, don't. Sit up an' wash him a' that side, or we s'll never have him done. Oh, Lizzie!

MRS HOLROYD (*sitting up, startled*): What – what?

GRANDMOTHER: Look at his poor hand!

*She holds up the right hand. The nails are bloody.*

---

[1] charming in manner or attractive in appearance

MRS HOLROYD: Oh, no! Oh, no! No!

*Both women weep.*

GRANDMOTHER (*after a while*): We maun[1] get on, Lizzie.

MRS HOLROYD (*sitting up*): I can't touch his hands.

GRANDMOTHER: But I'm his mother – there's nothing I couldn't do for him.

MRS HOLROYD: I don't care – I don't care.

GRANDMOTHER: Prithee, prithee, Lizzie, I don't want thee goin' off, Lizzie.

MRS HOLROYD (*moaning*): Oh, what shall I do!

GRANDMOTHER: Why, go thee an' get his feet washed. He's setting stiff, and how shall we get him laid out?

MRS HOLROYD, *sobbing, goes, kneels at the miner's feet, and begins pulling off the great boots.*

GRANDMOTHER: There's hardly a mark on him. Eh, what a man he is! I've had some fine sons, Lizzie, I've had some big men of sons.

MRS HOLROYD: He was always a lot whiter than me. And he used to chaff[2] me.

GRANDMOTHER: But his poor hands! I used to thank God for my children, but they're rods o' trouble, Lizzie, they are. Unfasten his belt, child. We mun get his things off soon, or else we s'll have such a job.

MRS HOLROYD, *having dragged off his boots, rises. She is weeping.*

**CURTAIN**

[1] must
[2] tease light-heartedly

# The Wedding

from the novel *The Rainbow*

It was a beautiful sunny day for the wedding, a muddy earth but a bright sky. They had three cabs and two big closed-in vehicles. Everybody crowded in the parlour in excitement. Anna was still upstairs. Her father kept taking a nip of brandy. He was handsome in his black coat and grey trousers. His voice was hearty but troubled. His wife came down in dark grey silk with lace, and a touch of peacock-blue in her bonnet. Her little body was very sure and definite. Brangwen was thankful she was there, to sustain him among all these people.

The carriages! The Nottingham Mrs Brangwen, in silk brocade, stands in the doorway saying who must go with whom. There is a great bustle. The front door is opened, and the wedding guests are walking down the garden path, whilst those still waiting peer through the window, and the little crowd at the gate gorps[1] and stretches. How funny such dressed-up people look in the winter sunshine!

They are gone – another lot! There begins to be more room. Anna comes down blushing and very shy, to be viewed in her white silk and her veil. Her mother-in-law surveys her objectively, twitches the white train, arranges the folds of the veil and asserts herself.

Loud exclamations from the window that the bridegroom's carriage has just passed.

"Where's your hat, father, and your gloves?" cries the bride, stamping her white slipper, her eyes flashing through her veil. He hunts round – his hair is ruffled. Everybody has gone but the bride and her father. He is ready – his face very red and daunted. Tilly[2] dithers in the little porch, waiting to open the door. A waiting woman walks round Anna, who asks:

"Am I all right?"

She is ready. She bridles herself and looks queenly. She waves her hand sharply to her father:

[1] stares
[2] Tilly is housekeeper at Tom Brangwen's farm

"Come here!"

He goes. She puts her hand very lightly on his arm, and holding her bouquet like a shower, stepping oh very graciously, just a little impatient with her father for being so red in the face, she sweeps slowly past the fluttering Tilly, and down the path. There are hoarse shouts at the gate, and all her floating foamy whiteness passes slowly into the cab.

Her father notices her slim ankle and foot as she steps up: a child's foot. His heart is hard with tenderness. But she is in ecstasies with herself for making such a lovely spectacle. All the way she sat flamboyant with bliss because it was all so lovely. She looked down solicitously at her bouquet: white roses and lilies-of-the-valley and tube-roses and maidenhair fern – very rich and cascade-like.

Her father sat bewildered with all this strangeness, his heart was so full it felt hard, and he couldn't think of anything.

The church was decorated for Christmas, dark with evergreens, cold and snowy with white flowers. He went vaguely down to the altar. How long was it since he had gone to be married himself? He was not sure whether he was going to be married now, or what he had come for. He had a troubled notion that he had to do something or other. He saw his wife's bonnet, and wondered why *she* wasn't there with him.

They stood before the altar. He was staring up at the east window, that glowed intensely, a sort of blue purple: it was deep blue glowing, and some crimson, the little yellow flowers held fast in veins of shadow, in a heavy web of darkness. How it burned alive in radiance among its black web.

"Who giveth this woman to be married to this man?" He felt somebody touch him. He started. The words still re-echoed in his memory, but were drawing off.

"Me," he said hastily.

Anna bent her head and smiled in her veil. How absurd he was!

Brangwen was staring away at the burning blue window at the back of the altar, and wondering vaguely, with pain, if he ever should get old, if he ever should feel arrived and established. He was here at Anna's wedding. Well, what right had he to feel responsible like a father? He was still as unsure and unfixed as when he had married himself. His wife and he! With a pang of anguish he realized what uncertainties they both were. He was a man of forty-five. Forty-five! In five more years fifty. Then sixty – then seventy – then it was finished. My God – and one still was so unestablished.

How did one grow old – how could one become confident? He wished he felt older. Why, what difference was there, as far as he felt matured or completed, between him now and him at his own wedding? He might be getting married over again – he and his wife. He felt himself tiny, a little, upright figure on a plain circled round with the immense, roaring sky: he and his wife, two little, upright figures walking across this plain, whilst the heavens shimmered and roared about them. When did one come to an end? In which direction was it finished? There was no end, no finish, only this roaring vast space. Did one never get old, never die? That was the clue. He exulted strangely, with torture. He would go on with his wife, he and she like two children camping in the plains. What was sure but the endless sky? But that was so sure, so boundless.

Still the royal blue colour burned and blazed and sported itself in the web of darkness before him, unwearyingly rich and splendid. How rich and splendid his own life was, red and burning and blazing and sporting itself in the dark meshes of his body: and his wife, how she glowed and burned dark within her meshes! Always it was so unfinished and unformed!

There was a loud noise of the organ. The whole party was trooping to the vestry. There was a blotted, scrawled book – and that young girl putting back her veil in her vanity, and laying her hand with the wedding-ring self-consciously conspicuous, and signing her name proudly because of the vain spectacle she made:

"Anna Theresa Lensky."[1]

"Anna Theresa Lensky" – what a vain, independent minx she was ! The bridegroom, slender in his black swallow-tail and grey trousers, solemn as a young solemn cat, was writing seriously:

"William Brangwen."[2]

That looked more like it.

"Come and sign, father," cried the imperious young hussy.

"Thomas Brangwen – clumsy-first," he said to himself as he signed.

Then his brother, a big, sallow fellow with black side-whiskers wrote:

[1] Anna Lensky was Tom Brangwen's step-daughter
[2] William was the son of Alfred Brangwen. Anna thus married her step-cousin

"Alfred Brangwen."

"How many more Brangwens?" said Tom Brangwen, ashamed of the too-frequent recurrence of his family name.

When they were out again in the sunshine, and he saw the frost hoary and blue among the long grass under the tomb-stones, the holly-berries overhead twinkling scarlet as the bells rang, the yew trees hanging their black, motionless, ragged boughs, everything seemed like a vision.

The marriage party went across the graveyard to the wall, mounted it by the little steps, and descended. Oh a vain white peacock of a bride perching herself on the top of the wall and giving her hand to the bridegroom on the other side, to be helped down! The vanity of her white, slim, daintily-stepping feet, and her arched neck. And the regal impudence with which she seemed to dismiss them all, the others, parents and wedding guests, as she went with her young husband.

In the cottage big fires were burning, there were dozens of glasses on the table, and holly and mistletoe hanging up. The wedding party crowded in, and Tom Brangwen, becoming roisterous, poured out drinks. Everybody must drink. The bells were ringing away against the windows.

"Lift your glasses up," shouted Tom Brangwen from the parlour, "lift your glasses up, an' drink to the hearth an' home – hearth an' home, an' may they enjoy it."

"Night an' day, an' may they enjoy it," shouted Frank Brangwen, in addition.

"Hammer an' tongs, and may they enjoy it," shouted Alfred Brangwen, the saturnine.

"Fill your glasses up, an' let's have it all over again," shouted Tom Brangwen.

"Hearth and home, an' may ye enjoy it."

There was a ragged shout of the company in response.

"Bed an' blessin', an' may ye enjoy it," shouted Frank Brangwen.

There was a swelling chorus in answer.

"Comin' and goin', an' may ye enjoy it," shouted the saturnine Alfred Brangwen, and the men roared by now boldly, and the woman said "Just hark, now!"

There was a touch of scandal in the air.

Then the party rolled off in the carriages, full speed back to the Marsh,[1] to a large meal of the high-tea order, which lasted

[1] the name of Tom Brangwen's farm

for an hour and a half. The bride and bridegroom sat at the head of the table, very prim and shining both of them, wordless, whilst the company raged down the table.

The Brangwen men had brandy in their tea, and were becoming unmanageable. The saturnine Alfred had glittering, unseeing eyes, and a strange, fierce way of laughing that showed his teeth. His wife glowered at him and jerked her head at him like a snake. He was oblivious. Frank Brangwen, the butcher, flushed and florid and handsome, roared echoes to his two brothers. Tom Brangwen in his solid fashion was letting himself go at last.

These three brothers dominated the whole company. Tom Brangwen wanted to make a speech. For the first time in his life, he must spread himself wordily.

"Marriage," he began, his eyes twinkling and yet quite profound for he was deeply serious and hugely amused at the same time, "marriage," he said, speaking in the slow, full-mouthed way of the Brangwens, "is what we're made for –"

"Let him talk," said Alfred Brangwen, slowly and inscrutably, "let him talk." Mrs Alfred darted indignant eyes at her husband.

"A man," continued Tom Brangwen, "enjoys being a man: for what purpose was he made a man, if not to enjoy it?"

"That a true word," said Frank, floridly.

"And likewise," continued Tom Brangwen, "a woman enjoys being a woman: at least we surmise she does –"

"Oh don't you bother – " called a farmer's wife.

"You may back your life they'd be summisin'," said Frank's wife.

"Now," continued Tom Brangwen, "for a man to be a man, it takes a woman –"

"It does that," said a woman grimly.

"And for a woman to be a woman, it takes a *man* – " continued Tom Brangwen.

"All speak up, men," chimed in a feminine voice.

"Therefore we have marriage," continued Tom Brangwen.

"Hold, hold," said Alfred Brangwen. "Don't run us off our legs."

And in dead silence the glasses were filled. The bride and bridegroom, two children, sat with intent, shining faces at the head of the table, abstracted.

"There's no marriage in heaven," went on Tom Brangwen; "but on earth there is marriage."

"That's the difference between 'em," said Alfred Brangwen, mocking.

"Alfred," said Tom Brangwen, "keep your remarks till afterwards, and then we'll thank you for them. – There's very little else, on earth, but marriage. You can talk about making money, or saving souls. You can save your own soul seven times over, and you may have a mint of money, but your soul goes gnawin', gnawin', gnawin', and it says there's something it must have. In heaven there is no marriage. But on earth there is marriage, else heaven drops out, and there's no bottom to it."

"Just hark you now," said Frank's wife.

"Go on, Thomas," said Alfred sardonically.

"*If* we've got to be Angels," went on Tom Brangwen, haranguing the company at large, "and if there is no such thing as a man nor a woman amongst them, then it seems to me as a married couple makes one Angel."

"It's the brandy," said Alfred Brangwen wearily.

"For," said Tom Brangwen, and the company was listening to the conundrum, "an Angel can't be *less* than a human being. And if it was only the soul of a man *minus* the man, then it would be less than a human being."

"Decidedly," said Alfred.

And a laugh went round the table. But Tom Brangwen was inspired.

"An Angel's got to be more than a human being," he continued. "So I say, an Angel is the soul of man and woman in one: they rise united at the Judgement Day, as one Angel –"

"Praising the Lord," said Frank.

"Praising the Lord," repeated Tom.

"And what about the women left over?" asked Alfred, jeering. The company was getting uneasy.

"That I can't tell. How do I know as there *is* anybody left over at the Judgement Day? Let that be. What I say is, that when a man's soul and a woman's soul unites together – that makes an Angel –"

"I dunno about souls. I know as one plus one makes three, sometimes," said Frank. But he had the laugh to himself.

"Bodies and souls, it's the same," said Tom.

"And what about your Missis, who was married afore you knew her?" asked Alfred, set on edge by this discourse.

"That I can't tell you. If I am to become an Angel, it'll be my married soul, and not my single soul. It'll not be the soul of me when I was a lad: for I hadn't a soul as would *make* an Angel then."

"I can always remember," said Frank's wife, "when our Harold was bad, he did nothink but see an angel at th' back o' th' lookin' glass. 'Look mother,' 'e said, 'at that angel!' 'Theer isn't no angel, my duck,' I said, but he wouldn't have it. I took th' lookin' glass off'n th' dressin' table, but it made no difference. He kep' on sayin' it was there. My word, it did give me a turn. I thought for sure as I'd lost him."

"I can remember," said another man, Tom's sister's husband, "my mother gave me a good hidin' once, for sayin' I'd got an angel up my nose. She seed me pokin', an' she said: 'What are you pokin' at your nose for – give over.' 'There's an angel up it,' I said, an' she fetched me such a wipe. But there it was. We used to call them thistle things 'angels' as wafts about. An' I'd pushed one o' these up my nose, for some reason or other."

"It's wonderful what children will get up their noses," said Frank's wife. "I c'n remember our Hemmie, she shoved one o' them bluebell things out o' th' middle of a bluebell, what they call 'candles,' up her nose, and oh we had some work! I'd seen her stickin' 'em on the end of her nose, like, but I never thought she'd be so soft as to shove it right up. She was a gel of eight or more. Oh my word, we got a crochet-hook an' I don't know what . . ."

Tom Brangwen's mood of inspiration began to pass away. He forgot all about it, and was soon roaring and shouting with the rest. Outside the wake came, singing the carols. They were invited into the bursting house. They had two fiddles and a piccolo. There in the parlour they played carols, and the whole company sang them at the top of its voice. Only the bride and bridegroom sat with shining eyes and strange, bright faces, and scarcely sang, or only with just moving lips.

The wake departed, and the guysers came. There was loud applause, and shouting and excitement as the old mystery play of St George,[1] in which every man present had acted as a boy, proceeded, with banging and thumping of club and dripping pan.

"By Jove, I got a crack once, when I was playin' Beelzebub,"[2] said Tom Brangwen, his eyes full of water with laughing. "It

[1] a play, mediaeval in origin, based on the legend of St George and the dragon
[2] The Devil: Satan

knocked all th' sense out of me as you'd crack an egg. But I tell you, when I come to, I played Old Johnny Roger[1] with St George, I did that."

He was shaking with laughter. Another knock came at the door. There was a hush.

"It's th' cab," said somebody from the door.

"Walk in," shouted Tom Brangwen, and a red-faced grinning man entered.

"Now you two, get yourselves ready an' off to blanket fair," shouted Tom Brangwen. "Strike a daisy, but if you're not off like a blink o' lightnin', you shanna go, you s'll sleep separate."

Anna rose silently and went to change her dress. Will Brangwen would have gone out, but Tilly came with his hat and coat. The youth was helped on.

"Well, here's luck, my boy," shouted his father.

"When th' fat's in th' fire, let it frizzle," admonished his uncle Frank.

"Fair and *softly* does it, fair an' *softly* does it," cried his aunt, Frank's wife, contrary.

"You don't want to fall over yourself," said his uncle by marriage. "You're not a bull at a gate."

"Let a man have his own road," said Tom Brangwen testily. "Don't be so free of your advice – it's his wedding this time, not yours."

"'E won't want many sign-posts," said his father. "There's some roads a man has to be led, an' there's some roads a boss-eyed man can only follow wi' one eye shut. But this road can't be lost by a blind man nor a boss-eyed man nor a cripple – and he's neither, thank God."

"Don't you be so sure o' your walkin' powers," cried Frank's wife. "There's many a man gets no further than half-way, nor can't to save his life, let him live for ever."

"Why, how do you know?" said Alfred.

"It's plain enough in th' looks o' some," retorted Lizzie, his sister-in-law.

The youth stood with a faint, half-hearing smile on his face. He was tense and abstracted. These things, or anything, scarcely touched him.

Anna came down, in her day dress, very elusive. She kissed

---

[1] an expression used to describe angry reaction—as we might say "I played hell with him."

everybody, men and women, Will Brangwen shook hands with everybody, kissed his mother, who began to cry, and the whole party went surging out to the cab.

The young couple were shut up, last injunction shouted at them.

"Drive on," shouted Tom Brangwen.

The cab rolled off. They saw the light diminish under the ash-trees. Then the whole party, quietened, went indoors.

"They'll have three good fires burning," said Tom Brangwen, looking at his watch. "I told Emma to make 'em up at nine, an' then leave the door on th' latch. It's only half-past. They'll have three fires burning, an' lamps lighted, an' Emma will ha' warmed th' bed wi' th' warmin' pan. So I s'd think they'll be all right."

The part was much quieter. They talked of the young couple.

"She said she didn't want a servant in," said Tom Brangwen. "The house isn't big enough, she'd always have the creature under her nose. Emma'll do what is wanted of her, an' they'll be to themselves."

"It's best," said Lizzie, "you're more free."

The party talked on slowly. Brangwen looked at his watch.

"Let's go an' give 'em a carol," he said. "We s'll find th' fiddles at the Cock an' Robin."

"Ay, come on," said Frank.

Alfred rose in silence. The brother-in-law and one of Will's brothers rose also.

The five men went out. The night was flashing with stars.

Sirius blazed like a signal at the side of the hill, Orion,[1] stately and magnificent, was sloping along.

Tom walked with his brother, Alfred. The men's heels rang on the ground.

"It's a fine night," said Tom.

"Ay," said Alfred.

"Nice to get out."

"Ay."

The brothers walked close together, the bond of blood strong between them. Tom always felt much the junior to Alfred.

"It's a long while since *you* left home," he said.

"Ay," said Alfred. "I though I was getting a bit oldish – but I'm not. It's the things you've got as gets worn out, it's not you

[1] Sirius and Orion are names of stars

yourself."

"Why, what's worn out?"

"Most folks as I've anything to do with – as has anything to do with me. They all break down. You've got to go on by yourself, if it's only to perdition. There's nobody going alongside even there."

Tom Brangwen meditated this.

"Maybe you was never broken in," he said.

"No, I never was," said Alfred proudly.

And Tom felt his elder brother despised him a little. He winced under it.

"Everybody's got a way of their own," he said, stubbornly. "It's only a dog as hasn't. An' them as can't take what they give an' give what they take, they must go by themselves, or get a dog as'll follow 'em."

"They can do without the dog," said his brother. And again Tom Brangwen was humble, thinking his brother was bigger than himself. But if he was, he was. And if it were finer to go alone, it was: he did not want to go for all that.

They went over the field, where a thin, keen wind blew round the ball of the hill, in the starlight. They came to the stile, and to the side of Anna's house. The lights were out, only on the blinds of the rooms downstairs, and of a bedroom upstairs, firelight flickered.

"We'd better leave 'em alone," said Alfred Brangwen.

"Nay, nay," said Tom. "We'll carol 'em, for th' last time."

And in a quarter of an hour's time, eleven silent, rather tipsy men scrambled over the wall, and into the garden by the yew-trees, outside the windows where faint firelight glowed on the blinds. There came a shrill sound, two violins and a piccolo shrilling on the frosty air.

"In the fields with their flocks abiding." A commotion of men's voices broke out singing in ragged unison.

Anna Brangwen had started up, listening, when the music began. She was afraid.

"It's the wake,"[1] he whispered.

She remained tense, her heart beating heavily, possessed with strange, strong fear. Then there came the burst of men's singing, rather uneven. She strained still, listening.

[1] ceremony observed on the eve of a religious festival – e.g. the singing of carols before Christmas. Here the carol also acts as a ceremony on the eve of Anna and Will's marriage night

"It's Dad," she said, in a low voice. They were silent, listening.
"And my father," he said.

She listened still. But she was sure. She sank down again into bed, into his arms. He held her very close, kissing her. The hymn rambled on outside, all the men singing their best, having forgotten everything else under the spell of the fiddles and the tune. The firelight glowed against the darkness in the room. Anna could hear her father singing with gusto.

"Aren't they silly," she whispered.

And they crept closer, closer together, hearts beating to one another. And even as the hymn rolled on, they ceased to hear it.

# A Sequence of Love Poems

## LAST WORDS TO MIRIAM

Yours is the sullen sorrow,
    The disgrace is also mine;
Your love was intense and thorough,
Mine was the love of a growing flower
    For the sunshine.

You had the power to explore me,
    Blossom me stalk by stalk;
You woke my spirit, you bore me
To consciousness, you gave me the dour
    Awareness – then I suffered a balk.

Body to body I could not
    Love you, although I would.
We kissed, we kissed though we should not.
You yielded, we threw the last cast,
    And it was no good.

You only endured, and it broke
    My craftsman's nerve.
No flesh responded to my stroke;
So I failed to give you the last
    Fine torture you did deserve.

You are shapely, you are adorned
    But opaque and null in the flesh;
Who, had I but. pierced with the thorned
Full anguish, perhaps had been cast
    In a lovely illumined mesh

Like a painted window; the best
    Fire passed through your flesh,
Undrossed it, and left it blest

In clean new awareness. But now
    Who shall take you afresh?

Now who will burn you free
    From your body's deadness and dross?
Since the fire has failed in me,
What man will stoop in your flesh to plough
    The shrieking cross?

A mute, nearly beautiful thing
    Is your face, that fills me with shame
As I see it hardening;
I should have been cruel enough to bring
    You through the flame.

## THE BRIDE

My love looks like a girl to-night,
    But she is old.
The plaits that lie along her pillow
    Are not gold,
But threaded with filigree silver,
    And uncanny cold.

She looks like a young maiden, since her brow
    Is smooth and fair;
Her cheeks are very smooth, her eyes are closed,
    She sleeps a rare,
Still, winsome sleep, so still, and so composed.

Nay, but she sleeps like a bride, and dreams her dreams
    Of perfect things.
She lies at last, the darling, in the shape of her dream;
    And her dead mouth sings
By its shape, like thrushes in clear evenings.

## PIANO

Softly, in the dusk, a woman is singing to me;
Taking me back down the vista of years, till I see
A child sitting under the piano, in the boom of the tingling strings
And pressing the small, poised feet of a mother who smiles as she
    sings.

43

In spite of myself, the insidious mastery of song
Betrays me back, till the heart of me weeps to belong
To the old Sunday evenings at home, with winter outside
And hymns in the cosy parlour, the tinkling piano our guide.

So now it is vain for the singer to burst into clamour
With the great black piano appassionato. The glamour
Of childish days is upon me, my manhood is cast
Down in the flood of remembrance, I weep like a child for the
    past.

## BEI[1] HENNEF

The little river twittering in the twilight,
The wan, wondering look of the pale sky,
    This is almost bliss.

And everything shut up and gone to sleep,
All the troubles and anxieties and pain
    Gone under the twilight.

Only the twilight now, and the soft 'Sh!' of the river
    That will last for ever.

And at last I know my love for you is here;
I can see it all, it is whole like the twilight,
It is large, so large, I could not see it before,
Because of the little lights and flickers and interruptions,
    Troubles, anxieties and pains.

    You are the call and I am the answer,
    You are the wish, and I the fulfilment,
    You are the night, and I the day.
      What else? it is perfect enough.
      It is perfectly complete,
      You and I,
      What more – ?

Strange, how we suffer in spite of this!

*Hennef am Rhein.*

[1] Near

## A YOUNG WIFE

The pain of loving you
Is almost more than I can bear.

I walk in fear of you.
The darkness starts up where
You stand, and the night comes through
Your eyes when you look at me.

Ah never before did I see
The shadows that live in the sun!

Now every tall glad tree
Turns round its back to the sun
And looks down on the ground, to see
The shadow it used to shun.

At the foot of each glowing thing
A night lies looking up.

Oh, and I want to sing
And dance, but I can't lift up
My eyes from the shadows: dark
They lie spilt round the cup.

What is it? – Hark
The faint fine seethe in the air!

Like the seething sound in a shell!
It is death still seething where
The wild-flower shakes its bell
And the skylark twinkles blue –

The pain of loving you
Is almost more than I can bear.

# A Letter to Mrs Hopkin[1]

*Mayrhofen* 138, *in Zillertal, Tirol, Austria.*
19 *Aug.,* 1912

You know that it is not forgetfulness makes us not write to you. You know you are one of the very, very few who will take us into your heart, together. So, if the months go by without your hearing, I know you will understand – I know you will be sticking by us, and we shall be depending on you. I wanted my sister to come and talk with you, but she wouldn't; you see, it is harder for her, she is young, and doesn't understand quite. And she is going to marry Eddie Clarke in the spring, is going to become a hard, respectable married woman – I think the thought of me is very bitter to her – and she won't speak of me to anybody. Only she, of all my people, knows. And I told Jessie[2] to leave her a chance of ridding herself of my influence: nobody else. Mrs— writes me – I told her I was with another woman – but no details. I am sorry for her, she is so ill.

Things have been hard, and worth it. There has been some sickening misery ... F. is to see the children, and stay with them, next Easter. It has been rather ghastly, that part of the affair. If only one didn't hurt so many people.

For ourselves, Frieda and I have struggled through some bad times into a wonderful naked intimacy, all kindled with warmth, that I know at last is love. I think I ought not to blame women, as I have done, but myself, for taking my love to the wrong woman, before now. Let every man find, keep on trying till he finds, the woman who can take him and whose love he can take, then who will grumble about men or about women. But the thing must be two-sided. At any rate, and whatever happens, I do love, and I am loved. I have given and I have taken – and that is eternal. Oh, if only people could marry properly; I believe in marriage.

Perhaps Frieda will have to come to London to see her husband, in the autumn. Then she might want you to help her. Would you go to London, if she needed you?

[1] see note on this letter on page 118
[2] Jessie Chambers

We think of spending the winter in Italy, somewhere on Lake Garda. We shall be awfully poor, but don't mind so long as we can manage. It is — and the children that are the trouble. You see he loves Frieda madly, and can't let go.

We walked from the Isarthal down here – or at least, quite a long way – F. and I – with our German shoulder-bags on our backs. We made tea and our meals by the rivers. Crossing the mountains, we got stranded one night. I found a lovely little wooden chapel, quite forsaken, and lit the candles, and looked at the hundreds of Ex Voto pictures[1] – so strange. Then I found F. had gone. But she came back to the shrine, saying we were at the top of the pass and there was a hay-hut in the Alpine meadow. There we slept that night. In the dawn, the peaks were round us, and we were, as it seemed, in a pot, with a green high meadow for a bottom.

Here we are lodging awhile in a farmhouse. A mountain stream rushes by just outside. It is icy and clear. We go out all day with our rucksacks – make fires, boil eggs, and eat the lovely fresh gruyère cheese that they make here. We are almost pure vegetarians. We go quite long ways up the valleys. The peaks of the mountains are covered with eternal snow. Water comes falling from a fearful height, and the cows, in the summer meadows, tinkle their bells. Sometimes F. undresses and lies in the sun – sometimes we bathe together – and we *can* be happy, nobody knows how happy.

There are millions of different bells: tiny harebells, big, black-purple mountain harebells, pale blue, hairy, strange creatures, blue and white Canterbury bells – then there's a great blue gentian, and flowers like monkey-musk. The Alpine roses are just over – and I believe we could find the edelweiss if we tried. Sometimes we drink with the mountain peasants in the Gasthaus,[2] and dance a little. And how we love each other – God only knows.

We shall be moving on soon, walking south, by the Brenner,[3] to Italy. If you write, address us at "Haus Vogelnest" – Wolfratshausen – bei München. F., with me, sends love.

Yours,

D. H. LAWRENCE

---

[1] pictures of local life and country scenes, painted by peasants on wood, framed in little frames and hung on the walls of the chapel

[2] restaurant

[3] the Brenner Pass

# The Prussian[1] Officer

I

They had marched more than thirty kilometres since dawn,
along the white, hot road where occasional thickets of trees
threw a moment of shade, then out into the glare again. On
either hand, the valley, wide and shallow, glittered with heat;
dark-green patches of rye, pale young corn, fallow and meadow
and black pine woods spread in a dull, hot diagram under a
glistening sky. But right in front the mountains ranged across,
pale blue and very still, snow gleaming gently out of the deep
atmosphere. And towards the mountains, on and on, the
regiment marched between the rye-fields and the meadows,
between the scraggy fruit trees set regularly on either side the
high road. The burnished, dark-green rye threw off a suffocating
heat, the mountains drew gradually nearer and more distinct.
While the feet of the soldiers grew hotter, sweat ran through
their hair under their helmets, and their knapsacks could burn
no more in contact with their shoulders, but seemed instead to
give off a cold, prickly sensation.

He walked on and on in silence, staring at the mountains
ahead, that rose sheer out of the land, and stood fold behind
fold, half earth, half heaven, the heaven, the barrier with slits
of soft snow, in the pale, bluish peaks.

He could now walk almost without pain. At the start, he had
determined not to limp. It had made him sick to take the first
steps, and during the first mile or so, he had compressed his
breath, and the cold drops of sweat had stood on his forehead.
But he had walked it off. What were they after all but bruises!
He had looked at them, as he was getting up: deep bruises on
the backs of his thighs. And since he had made his first step in
the morning, he had been conscious of them, till now he had a

[1] Prussia, originally a separate state in North Germany, was the cradle of
German militarism. Its nineteenth century leader, Bismarck, brought about
the unification of Germany

tight, hot place in his chest, with suppressing the pain, and holding himself in. There seemed no air when he breathed. But he walked almost lightly.

The Captain's hand had trembled at taking his coffee at dawn: his orderly[1] saw it again. And he saw the fine figure of the Captain wheeling on horseback at the farmhouse ahead, a handsome figure in pale-blue uniform with facings of scarlet, and the metal gleaming on the black helmet and the sword-scabbard, and dark streaks of sweat coming on the silky bay horse. The orderly felt he was connected with that figure moving so suddenly on horseback: he followed it like a shadow, mute and inevitable and damned by it. And the officer was always aware of the tramp of the company behind, the march of his orderly among the men.

The Captain was a tall man of about forty, grey at the temples. He had a handsome, finely-knit figure, and was one of the best horsemen in the West. His orderly, having to rub him down, admired the amazing riding-muscles of his loins.

For the rest, the orderly scarcely noticed the officer any more than he noticed himself. It was rarely he saw his master's face: he did not look at it. The Captain had reddish-brown stiff hair, that he wore short upon his skull. His moustache was also cut short and bristly over a full, brutal mouth. His face was rather rugged, the cheeks thin. Perhaps the man was the more handsome for the deep lines in his face, the irritable tension of his brow, which gave him the look of a man who fights with life. His fair eyebrows stood bushy over light-blue eyes that were always flashing with cold fire.

He was a Prussian aristocrat, haughty and overbearing. But his mother had been a Polish countess. Having made too many gambling debts when he was young, he had ruined his prospects in the Army, and remained an infantry[2] captain. He had never married: his position did not allow of it, and no woman had ever moved him to it. His time he spent riding – occasionally he rode one of his own horses at the races – and at the officers' club. Now and then he took himself a mistress. But after such an event, he returned to duty with his brow still more tense, his eyes still more hostile and irritable. With the men, however, he

[1] an orderly is a private soldier who acts as an officer's messenger and general servant

[2] foot soldier (as opposed to mounted soldier – i.e. cavalry)

was merely impersonal, though a devil when roused; so that, on the whole, they feared him, but had no great aversion from him. They accepted him as the inevitable.

To his orderly he was at first cold and just and indifferent: he did not fuss over trifles. So that his servant knew practically nothing about him, except just what orders he would give, and how he wanted them obeyed. That was quite simple. Then the change gradually came.

The orderly was a youth of about twenty-two, of medium height, and well built. He had strong, heavy limbs, was swarthy, with a soft, black, young moustache. There was something altogether warm and young about him. He had firmly marked eyebrows over dark, expressionless eyes, that seemed never to have thought, only to have received life direct through his senses, and acted straight from instinct.

Gradually the officer had become aware of his servant's young, vigorous, unconscious presence about him. He could not get away from the sense of the youth's person, while he was in attendance. It was like a warm flame upon the older man's tense, rigid body, that had become almost unliving, fixed. There was something so free and self-contained about him, and something in the young fellow's movement, that made the officer aware of him. And this irritated the Prussian. He did not choose to be touched into life by his servant. He might easily have changed his man, but he did not. He now very rarely looked direct at his orderly, but kept his face averted, as if to avoid seeing him. And yet as the young soldier moved unthinking about the apartment, the elder watched him, and would notice the movement of his strong young shoulders under the blue cloth, the bend of his neck. And it irritated him. To see the soldier's young, brown, shapely peasant's hand grasp the loaf or the wine-bottle sent a flash of hate or of anger through the elder man's blood. It was not that the youth was clumsy: it was rather the blind, instinctive sureness of movement of an unhampered young animal that irritated the officer to such a degree.

Once, when a bottle of wine had gone over, and the red gushed out on to the tablecloth, the officer had started up with an oath, and his eyes, bluey like fire, had held those of the confused youth for a moment. It was a shock for the young soldier. He felt something sink deeper, deeper into his soul, where nothing had ever gone before. It left him rather blank and wondering. Some of his natural completeness in himself was gone, a little uneasiness took its place. And from that time an undiscovered feeling had held between the two men.

Henceforward the orderly was afraid of really meeting his master. His subconsciousness remembered those steely blue eyes and the harsh brows, and did not intend to meet them again. So he always stared past his master, and avoided him. Also, in a little anxiety, he waited for the three months to have gone, when his time would be up. He began to feel a constraint in the Captain's presence, and the soldier even more than the officer wanted to be left alone, in his neutrality as servant.

He had served the Captain for more than a year, and knew his duty. This he performed easily, as if it were natural to him. The officer and his commands he took for granted, as he took the sun and the rain, and he served as a matter of course. It did not implicate him personally.

But now if he were going to be forced into a personal interchange with his master he would be like a wild thing caught, he felt he must get away.

But the influence of the young soldier's being had penetrated through the officer's stiffened discipline, and perturbed the man in him. He, however, was a gentleman, with long, fine hands and cultivated movements, and was not going to allow such a thing as the stirring of his innate self. He was a man of passionate temper, who had always kept himself suppressed. Occasionally there had been a duel, an outburst before the soldiers. He knew himself to be always on the point of breaking out. But he kept himself hard to the idea of the Service. Whereas the young soldier seemed to live out his warm, full nature, to give it off in his very movements, which had a certain zest, such as wild animals have in free movement. And this irritated the officer more and more.

In spite of himself, the Captain could not regain his neutrality of feeling towards his orderly. Nor could he leave the man alone. In spite of himself, he watched him, gave him sharp orders, tried to take up as much of his time as possible. Sometimes he flew into a rage with the young soldier, and bullied him. Then the orderly shut himself off; as it were out of earshot, and waited, with sullen, flushed face, for the end of the noise. The words never pierced to his intelligence, he made himself, protectively, impervious to the feelings of his master.

He had a scar on his left thumb, a deep seam going across

the knuckle. The officer had long suffered from it, and wanted to do something to it. Still it was there, ugly and brutal on the young, brown hand. At last the Captain's reserve gave way. One day, as the orderly was smoothing out the tablecloth, the officer pinned down his thumb with a pencil, asking:

"How did you come by that?"

The young man winced and drew back at attention.

"A wood axe, Herr Hauptmann," [1] he answered.

The officer waited for further explanation. None came. The orderly went about his duties. The elder man was sullenly angry. His servant avoided him. And the next day he had to use all his will-power to avoid seeing the scarred thumb. He wanted to get hold of it and—— A hot flame ran in his blood.

He knew his servant would soon be free, and would be glad. As yet, the soldier had held himself off from the elder man. The Captain grew madly irritable. He could not rest when the soldier was away, and when he was present, he glared at him with tormented eyes. He hated those fine, black brows over the unmeaning, dark eyes, he was infuriated by the free move-ment of the handsome limbs, which no military discipline could make stiff. And he became harsh and cruelly bullying, using contempt and satire. The young soldier only grew more mute and expressionless.

"What cattle were you bred by, that you can't keep straight eyes? Look me in the eyes when I speak to you."

And the soldier turned his dark eyes to the other's face, but there was no sight in them: he stared with the slightest possible cast, holding back his sight, perceiving the blue of his master's eyes, but receiving no look from them. And the elder man went pale, and his reddish eyebrows twitched. He gave his order, barrenly.

Once he flung a heavy military glove into the young soldier's face. Then he had the satisfaction of seeing the black eyes flare up into his own, like a blaze when straw is thrown on a fire. And he had laughed with a little tremor and a sneer.

But there were only two months more. The youth instinctively tried to keep himself intact: he tried to serve the officer as if the latter were an abstract authority and not a man. All his instinct was to avoid personal contact, even definite hate. But in spite of himself the hate grew, responsive to the officer's

[1] Captain

52

passion. However, he put it in the background. When he had left the Army he could dare acknowledge it. By nature he was active, and had many friends. He thought what amazing good fellows they were. But, without knowing it, he was alone. Now this solitariness was intensified. It would carry him through his term. But the officer seemed to be going irritably insane, and the youth was deeply frightened.

The soldier had a sweetheart, a girl from the mountains, independent and primitive. The two walked together, rather silently. He went with her, not to talk, but to have his arm round her, and for the physical contact. This eased him, made it easier for him to ignore the Captain; for he could rest with her held fast against his chest. And she, in some unspoken fashion, was there for him. They loved each other.

The Captain perceived it, and was mad with irritation. He kept the young man engaged all the evenings long, and took pleasure in the dark look that came on his face. Occasionally, the eyes of the two men met, those of the younger sullen and dark, doggedly unalterable, those of the elder sneering with restless contempt.

The officer tried hard not to admit the passion that had got hold of him. He would not know that his feeling for his orderly was anything but that of a man incensed by his stupid, perverse servant. So, keeping quite justified and conventional in his consciousness, he let the other thing run on. His nerves, however, were suffering. At last he slung the end of a belt in his servant's face. When he saw the youth start back, the pain-tears in his eyes and the blood on his mouth, he had felt at once a thrill of deep pleasure and of shame.

But this, he acknowledged to himself, was a thing he had never done before. The fellow was too exasperating. His own nerves must be going to pieces. He went away for some days with a woman.

It was a mockery of pleasure. He simply did not want the woman. But he stayed on for his time. At the end of it, he came back in an agony of irritation, torment, and misery. He rode all the evening, then came straight in to supper. His orderly was out. The officer sat with his long, fine hands lying on the table, perfectly still, and all his blood seemed to be corroding.

At last his servant entered. He watched the strong, easy young figure, the fine eyebrows, the thick black hair. In a week's time the youth had got back his old well-being. The hands of the officer twitched and seemed to be full of mad flame. The young man stood at attention, unmoving, shut off.

The meal went in silence. But the orderly seemed eager. He made a clatter with the dishes.

"Are you in a hurry?" asked the officer, watching the intent, warm face of his servant. The other did not reply.

"Will you answer my question?" said the Captain.

"Yes, sir," replied the orderly, standing with his pile of deep Army plates. The Captain waited, looked at him, then asked again:

"Are you in a hurry?"

"Yes, sir," came the answer, that sent a flash through the listener.

"For what?"

"I was going out, sir."

"I want you this evening."

There was a moment's hesitation. The officer had a curious stiffness of countenance.

"Yes, sir," replied the servant, in his throat.

"I want you to-morrow evening also – in fact you may consider your evenings occupied, unless I give you leave."

The mouth with the young moustache set close.

"Yes, sir," answered the orderly, loosening his lips for a moment.

He again turned to the door.

"And why have you a piece of pencil in your ear?"

The orderly hesitated, then continued on his way without answering. He set the plates in a pile outside the door, took the stump of pencil from his ear, and put it in his pocket. He had been copying a verse for his sweetheart's birthday card. He returned to finish clearing the table. The officer's eyes were dancing, he had a little, eager smile.

"Why have you a piece of pencil in your ear?" he asked. The orderly took his hands full of dishes. His master was standing near the great green stove, a little smile on his face, his chin thrust forward. When the young soldier saw him his heart suddenly ran hot. He felt blind. Instead of answering, he turned dazedly to the door. As he was crouching to set down the dishes, he was pitched forward by a kick from behind. The pots went in a stream down the stairs, he clung to the pillar of the banisters. And as he was rising he was kicked heavily again and again, so that he clung sickly to the post for some moments. His master had gone swiftly into the room and closed the door. The maid-servant downstairs looked up the staircase and made a mocking face at the crockery disaster.

The officer's heart was plunging. He poured himself a glass of wine, part of which he spilled on the floor, and gulped the remainder, leaning against the cool, green stove. He heard his man collecting the dishes from the stairs. Pale, as if intoxicated, he waited. The servant entered again. The Captain's heart gave a pang, as of pleasure, seeing the young fellow bewildered and uncertain on his feet with pain.

"Schöner!" he said.

The soldier was a little slower in coming to attention.

"Yes, sir!"

The youth stood before him, with pathetic young moustache, and fine eyebrows very distinct on his forehead of dark marble.

"I asked you a question."

"Yes, sir."

The officer's tone bit like acid.

"Why had you a pencil in your ear?"

Again the servant's heart ran hot, and he could not breathe. With dark, strained eyes, he looked at the officer, as if fascinated. And he stood there sturdily planted, unconscious. The withering smile came into the Captain's eyes, and he lifted his foot.

"I forgot it – sir," panted the solder, his dark eyes fixed on the other man's dancing blue ones.

"What was it doing there?"

He saw the young man's breast heaving as he made an effort for words.

"I had been writing."

"Writing what?"

Again the soldier looked him up and down. The officer could hear him panting. The smile came into the blue eyes. The soldier worked his dry throat, but could not speak. Suddenly the smile lit like a flame on the officer's face, and a kick came heavily against the orderly's thigh. The youth moved sideways. His face went dead, with two black, staring eyes.

"Well?" said the officer.

The orderly's mouth had gone dry, and his tongue rubbed in it as on dry brown-paper. He worked his throat. The officer raised his foot. The servant went stiff.

"Some poetry, sir," came the crackling, unrecognisable sound of his voice.

"Poetry, what poetry?" asked the Captain, with a sickly smile.

Again there was the working in the throat. The Captain's heart had suddenly gone down heavily, and he stood sick and tired.

"For my girl, sir," he heard the dry, inhuman sound.

"Oh!" he said, turning away. "Clear the table."

"Click!" went the soldier's throat; then again, "click!" and then the half-articulate:

"Yes, sir."

The young soldier was gone, looking old, and walking heavily.

The officer, left alone, held himself rigid, to prevent himself from thinking. His instinct warned him that he must not think. Deep inside him was the intense gratification of his passion, still working powerfully. Then there was a counteracting, a horrible breaking down of something inside him, a whole agony of reaction. He stood there for an hour motionless, a chaos of sensations, but rigid with a will to keep blank his consciousness, to prevent his mind grasping. And he held himself so until the worst of the stress had passed, when he began to drink, drank himself to an intoxication, till he slept obliterated. When he woke in the morning he was shaken to the base of his nature. But he had fought off the realization of what he had done. He had prevented his mind from taking it in, had suppressed it along with his instincts, and the conscious man had nothing to do with it. He felt only as after a bout of intoxication, weak, but the affair itself all dim and not to be recovered. Of the drunkenness of his passion he successfully refused remembrance. And when his orderly appeared with coffee, the officer assumed the same self he had had the morning before. He refused the event of the past night – denied it had ever been – and was successful in his denial. He had not done any such thing – not he himself. Whatever there might be lay at the door of a stupid insubordinate servant.

The orderly had gone about in a stupor all the evening. He drank some beer because he was parched, but not much, the alcohol made his feeling come back, and he could not bear it. He was dulled, as if nine-tenths of the ordinary man in him were inert. He crawled about disfigured. Still, when he thought of the kick, he went sick, and when he thought of the threat of more kicking, in the room afterwards, his heart went hot and faint, and he panted, remembering the one that had come. He had been forced to say: "For my girl." He was much too done even to want to cry. His mouth hung slightly open, like an idiot's. He felt vacant, and wasted. So, he wandered at his work, painfully, and very slowly and clumsily, fumbling blindly with the brushes, and finding it difficult, when he sat down, to summon the energy to move again. His limbs, his jaw, were slack and nerveless. But he was very tired. He got to bed at last, and slept inert, relaxed, in a sleep that was rather stupor than slumber, a dead night of stupefaction shot through with gleams of anguish.

In the morning were the manœuvres. But he woke even before the bugle sounded. The painful ache in his chest, the dryness of his throat, the awful steady feeling of misery made his eyes come awake and dreary at once. He knew, without thinking, what had happened. And he knew that the day had come again, when he must go on with his round. The last bit of darkness was being pushed out of the room. He would have to move his inert body and go on. He was so young, and had known so little trouble, that he was bewildered. He only wished it would stay night, so that he could lie still, covered up by the darkness. And yet nothing would prevent the day from coming, nothing would save him from having to get up and saddle the Captain's horse, and make the Captain's coffee. It was there, inevitable. And then, he thought, it was impossible. Yet they would not leave him free. He must go and take the coffee to the Captain. He was too stunned to understand it. He only knew it was inevitable – inevitable, however long he lay inert.

At last, after heaving at himself, for he seemed to be a mass of inertia, he got up. But he had to force every one of his movements from behind, with his will. He felt lost, and dazed, and helpless. Then he clutched hold of the bed, the pain was so keen. And looking at his thighs he saw the darker bruises on his swarthy flesh, and he knew that if he pressed one of his fingers on one of of the bruises, he should faint. But he did not want to faint – he did not want anybody to know. No one should ever know. It was between him and the Captain. There were only the two people in the world now – himself and the Captain.

Slowly, economically, he got dressed and forced himself to walk. Everything was obscure, except just what he had his hands on. But he managed to get through his work. The very pain revived his dull senses. The worst remained yet. He took the tray and went up to the Captain's room. The officer, pale and heavy, sat at the table. The orderly, as he saluted, felt himself put out of existence. He stood still for a moment submitting to his own nullification – then he gathered himself, seemed to regain himself, and then the Captain began to grow vague, unreal, and the younger soldier's heart beat up. He clung to this situation – that the Captain did not exist – so that he himself might live. But when he saw his officer's hand tremble as he took the coffee, he felt everything falling shattered. And he went away, feeling as if he himself were coming to pieces disintegrated. And when the Captain was there on horseback, giving orders, while he himself stood, with rifle and knapsack, sick with pain, he felt as if he must shut his eyes – as if he must shut his eyes on everything. It was only the long agony of marching with a parched throat that filled him with one single, sleep-heavy intention: to save himself.

## II

He was getting used even to his parched throat. That the snowy peaks were radiant among the sky, that the whity-green glacier-river twisted through its pale shoals, in the valley below, seemed almost supernatural. But he was going mad with fear and thirst. He plodded on uncomplaining. He did not want to speak, not to anybody. There were two gulls, like flakes of water and snow, over the river. The scent of green rye soaked in sunshine came like a sickness. And the march continued, monotonously, almost like a bad sleep.

At the next farmhouse, which stood low and broad near the high road, tubs of water had been put out. The soldiers clustered round to drink. They took off their helmets, and the steam mounted from their wet hair. The Captain sat on horseback, watching. He needed to see his orderly. His helmet threw a dark shadow over his light, fierce eyes, but his moustache and mouth and chin were distinct in the sunshine. The orderly must move under the presence of the figure of the horseman. It was not that he was afraid, or cowed. It was as if he was disembowelled, made empty, like an empty shell. He felt himself as nothing, a shadow creeping under the sunshine. And, thirsty as he was, he could scarcely drink, feeling the Captain near him. He would not take off his helmet to wipe his wet hair. He wanted to stay in shadow, not to be forced into consciousness. Starting, he saw the light heel of the officer prick the belly of the horse; the Captain cantered away, and he himself could relapse into vacancy.

Nothing, however, could give him back his living place in the hot, bright morning. He felt like a gap among it all. Whereas the Captain was prouder, overriding. A hot flash went through the young servant's body. The Captain was firmer and prouder with life, he himself was empty as a shadow. Again the flash went through him, dazing him out. But his heart ran a little firmer.

The company turned up the hill, to make a loop for the return. Below, from among the trees, the farm-bell clanged. He saw the labourers, mowing bare-foot at the thick grass, leave off their work and go downhill, their scythes hanging over their shoulders, like long, bright claws curving down behind them. They seemed like dream-people, as if they had no relation to himself. He felt as in a blackish dream: as if all the other things were there and had form, but he himself was only a consciousness, a gap that could think and perceive.

The soldiers were tramping silently up the glaring hill-side. Gradually his head began to revolve, slowly, rhythmically. Sometimes it was dark before his eyes, as if he saw this world through a smoked glass, frail shadows and unreal. It gave him a pain in his head to walk.

The air was too scented, it gave no breath. All the lush green-stuff seemed to be issuing its sap, till the air was deathly, sickly with the smell of greenness. There was the perfume of clover, like pure honey and bees. Then there grew a faint acrid tang – they were near the beeches; and then a queer clattering noise, and a suffocating, hideous smell; they were passing a flock of sheep, a shepherd in a black smock, holding his crook. Why should the sheep huddle together under this fierce sun? He felt that the shepherd would not see him, though he could see the shepherd.

At last there was the halt. They stacked rifles in a conical stack, put down their kit in a scattered circle around it, and dispersed a little, sitting on a small knoll high on the hill-side. The chatter began. The soldiers were steaming with heat, but were lively. He sat still, seeing the blue mountains rising upon the land, twenty kilometres away. There was a blue fold in the ranges, then out of that, at the foot, the broad, pale bed of the river, stretches of whity-green water between pinkish-grey shoals among the dark pine woods. There it was, spread out a long way off. And it seemed to come downhill, the river. There was a raft being steered, a mile away. It was a strange country. Nearer, a red-roofed, broad farm with white base and square dots of windows crouched beside the wall of beech foliage on the wood's edge. There were long strips of rye and clover and pale green corn. And just at his feet, below the knoll, was a darkish bog, where globe flowers stood breathless still on their slim stalks. And some of the pale gold bubbles were burst, and a broken fragment hung in the air. He thought he was going to sleep.

Suddenly something moved into his coloured mirage before his eyes. The Captain, a small, light-blue and scarlet figure, was trotting evenly between the strips of corn, along the level brow of the hill. And the man making flag-signals was coming on. Proud and sure moved the horseman's figure, the quick, bright thing, in which was concentrated all the light of this morning, which for the rest lay fragile, shining shadow. Submissive, apathetic, the young soldier sat and stared. But as the horse slowed to a walk, coming up the last steep path, the great flash flared over the body and soul of the orderly. He sat waiting. The back of his head felt as if it were weighted with a heavy piece of fire. He did not want to eat. His hands trembled slightly as he moved them. Meanwhile the officer on horseback was approaching slowly and proudly. The tension grew in the orderly's soul. Then again, seeing the Captain ease himself on the saddle, the flash blazed through him.

The Captain looked at the patch of light blue and scarlet, and dark head, scattered closely on the hill-side. It pleased him. The command pleased him. And he was feeling proud. His orderly was among them in common subjection. The officer rose a little on his stirrups to look. The young soldier sat with averted, dumb face. The Captain relaxed on his seat. His slim-legged, beautiful horse, brown as a beech nut, walked proudly uphill. The Captain passed into the zone of the company's atmosphere: a hot smell of men, of sweat, of leather. He knew it very well. After a word with the lieutenant, he went a few paces higher, and sat there, a dominant figure, his sweat-marked horse swishing its tail, while he looked down on his men, on his orderly, a nonentity among the crowd.

The young soldier's heart was like fire in his chest, and he breathed with difficulty. The officer, looking downhill, saw three of the young soldiers, two pails of water between them, staggering across a sunny green field. A table had been set up under a tree, and there the slim lieutenant stood importantly busy. Then the Captain summoned himself to an act of courage. He called his orderly.

The flame leapt into the young soldier's throat as he heard the command, and he rose blindly, stifled. He saluted, standing below the officer. He did not look up. But there was the flicker in the Captain's voice.

"Go to the inn and fetch me . . ." the officer gave his commands. "Quick!" he added.

At the last word, the heart of the servant leapt with a flash, and he felt the strength come over his body. But he turned in mechanical obedience, and set off at a heavy run downhill, looking almost like a bear, his trousers bagging over his military boots. And the officer watched this blind, plunging run all the way.

But it was only the outside of the orderly's body that was obeying so humbly and mechanically. Inside had gradually accumulated a core into which all the energy of that young life was compact and concentrated. He executed his commission, and plodded quickly back uphill. There was a pain in his head as he walked that made him twist his features unknowingly. But hard there in the centre of his chest was himself, himself, firm, and not to be plucked to pieces.

The Captain had gone up into the wood. The orderly plodded through the hot, powerfully smelling zone of the company's atmosphere. He had a curious mass of energy inside him now. The Captain was less real than himself. He approached the green entrance to the wood. There, in the half-shade, he saw the horse standing, the sunshine and the flickering shadow of leaves dancing over his brown body. There was a clearing where timber had lately been felled. Here, in the gold-green shade beside the brilliant cup of sunshine, stood two figures, blue and pink, the bits of pink showing out plainly. The Captain was talking to his lieutenant.

The orderly stood on the edge of the bright clearing, where great trunks of trees, stripped and glistening, lay stretched like naked, brown-skinned bodies. Chips of wood littered the trampled floor, like splashed light, and the bases of the felled trees stood here and there, with their raw, level tops. Beyond was the brilliant, sunlit green of a beech.

"Then I will ride forward," the orderly heard his Captain say. The lieutenant saluted and strode away. He himself went forward. A hot flash passed through his belly, as he tramped towards his officer.

The Captain watched the rather heavy figure of the young

soldier stumble forward, and his veins, too, ran hot. This was to be man to man between them. He yielded before the solid, stumbling figure with bent head. The orderly stooped and put the food on a level-sawn tree-base. The Captain watched the glistening, sun-inflamed, naked hands. He wanted to speak to the young soldier, but could not. The servant propped a bottle against his thigh, pressed open the cork, and poured out the beer into the mug. He kept his head bent. The Captain accepted the mug.

"Hot!" he said, as if amiably.

The flame sprang out of the orderly's heart, nearly suffocating him.

"Yes, sir," he replied, between shut teeth.

And he heard the sound of the Captain's drinking, and he clenched his fists, such a strong torment came into his wrists. Then came the faint clang of the closing of the pot-lid. He looked up. The Captain was watching him. He glanced swiftly away. Then he saw the officer stoop and take a piece of bread from the tree-base. Again the flash of flame went through the young soldier, seeing the stiff body stoop beneath him, and his hands jerked. He looked away. He could feel the officer was nervous. The bread fell as it was being broken. The officer ate the other piece. The two men stood tense and still, the master laboriously chewing his bread, the servant staring with averted face, his fist clenched.

Then the young soldier started. The officer had pressed open the lid of the mug again. The orderly watched the lip of the mug, and the white hand that clenched the handle, as if he were fascinated. It was raised. The youth followed it with his eyes. And then he saw the thin, strong throat of the elder man moving up and down as he drank, the strong jaw working. And the instinct which had been jerking at the young man's wrists suddenly jerked free. He jumped, feeling as if it were rent in two by a strong flame.

The spur of the officer caught in a tree root, he went down backwards with a crash, the middle of his back thudding sickeningly against a sharp-edged tree-base, the pot flying away. And in a second the orderly, with serious, earnest young face, and underlip between his teeth, had got his knee in the officer's chest and was pressing the chin backward over the farther edge of the tree-stump, pressing, with all his heart behind in a passion of relief, the tension of his wrists exquisite with relief.

And with the base of his palms he shoved at the chin, with all his might. And it was pleasant, too, to have that chin, that hard jaw already slightly rough with beard, in his hands. He did not relax one hair's breadth, but, all the force of all his blood exulting in his thrust, he shoved back the head of the other man, till there was a little "cluck" and a crushing sensation. Then he felt as if his head went to vapour. Heavy convulsions shook the body of the officer, frightening and horrifying the young soldier. Yet it pleased him, too, to repress them. It pleased him to keep his hands pressing back the chin, to feel the chest of the other man yield in expiration to the weight of his strong, young knees, to feel the hard twitchings of the prostrate body jerking his own whole frame, which was pressed down on it.

But it went still. He could look into the nostrils of the other man, the eyes he could scarcely see. How curiously the mouth was pushed out, exaggerating the full lips, and the moustache bristling up from them. Then, with a start, he noticed the nostrils gradually filled with blood. The red brimmed, hesitated, ran over, and went in a thin trickle down the face to the eyes.

It shocked and distressed him. Slowly, he got up. The body twitched and sprawled there, inert. He stood and looked at it in silence. It was a pity *it* was broken. It represented more than the thing which had kicked and bullied him. He was afraid to look at the eyes. They were hideous now, only the whites showing, and the blood running to them. The face of the orderly was drawn with horror at the sight. Well, it was so. In his heart he was satisfied. He had hated the face of the Captain. It was extinguished now. There was a heavy relief in the orderly's soul. That was as it should be. But he could not bear to see the long, military body lying broken over the tree-base, the fine fingers crisped. He wanted to hide it away.

Quickly, busily, he gathered it up and pushed it under the felled tree trunks, which rested their beautiful, smooth length either end on the logs. The face was horrible with blood. He covered it with the helmet. Then he pushed the limbs straight and decent, and brushed the dead leaves off the fine cloth of the uniform. So, it lay quite still in the shadow under there. A little strip of sunshine ran along the breast, from a chink between the logs. The orderly sat by it for a few moments. Here his own life also ended.

Then, through his daze, he heard the lieutenant, in a loud

voice, explaining to the men outside the wood, that they were to suppose the bridge on the river below was held by the enemy. Now they were to march to the attack in such and such a manner. The lieutenant had no gift of expression. The orderly, listening from habit, got muddled. And when the lieutenant began it all again he ceased to hear.

He knew he must go. He stood up. It surprised him that the leaves were glittering in the sun, and the chips of wood reflecting white from the ground. For him a change had come over the world. But for the rest it had not – all seemed the same. Only he had left it. And he could not go back. It was his duty to return with the beer-pot and the bottle. He could not. He had left all that. The lieutenant was still hoarsely explaining. He must go, or they would overtake him. And he could not bear contact with anyone now.

He drew his fingers over his eyes, trying to find out where he was. Then he turned away. He saw the horse standing in the path. He went up to it and mounted. It hurt him to sit in the saddle. The pain of keeping his seat occupied him as they cantered through the wood. He would not have minded anything, but he could not get away from the sense of being divided from the others. The path led out of the trees. On the edge of the wood he pulled up and stood watching. There in the spacious sunshine of the valley soldiers were moving in a little swarm. Every now and then, a man harrowing on a strip of fallow shouted to his oxen, at the turn. The village and the white-towered church was small in the sunshine. And he no longer belonged to it – he sat there, beyond, like a man outside in the dark. He had gone out from everyday life into the unknown and he could not, he even did not want to go back.

Turning from the sun-blazing valley, he rode deep into the wood. Trees trunks, like people standing grey and still, took no notice as he went. A doe, herself a moving bit of sunshine and shadow, went running through the flecked shade. There were bright green rents in the foliage. Then it was all pine wood, dark and cool. And he was sick with pain, and had an intolerable great pulse in his head, and he was sick. He had never been ill in his life. He felt lost, quite dazed with all this.

Trying to get down from the horse, he fell, astonished at the pain and his lack of balance. The horse shifted uneasily. He jerked its bridle and sent it cantering jerkily away. It was his last connection with the rest of things.

But he only wanted to lie down and not be disturbed. Stumbling through the trees, he came on a quiet place where beeches and pine trees grew on a slope. Immediately he had lain down and closed his eyes, his consciousness went racing on without him. A big pulse of sickness beat in him as if it throbbed through the whole earth. He was burning with dry heat. But he was too busy, too tearingly active in the incoherent race of delirium to observe.

### III

He came to with a start. His mouth was dry and hard, his heart beat heavily, but he had not the energy to get up. His heart beat heavily. Where was he? – the barracks – at home? There was something knocking. And, making an effort, he looked round – trees, and litter of greenery, and reddish, bright, still pieces of sunshine on the floor. He did not believe he was himself, he did not believe what he saw. Something was knocking. He made a struggle towards consciousness, but relapsed. Then he struggled again. And gradually his surroundings fell into relationship with himself. He knew, and a great pang of fear went through his heart. Somebody was knocking. He could see the heavy, black rags of a fir tree overhead. Then everything went black. Yet he did not believe he had closed his eyes. He had not. Out of the blackness sight slowly emerged again. And someone was knocking. Quickly, he saw the blood-disfigured face of his Captain, which he hated. And he held himself still with horror. Yet, deep inside the physical delirium got hold of him. Someone was knocking. He lay perfectly still, as if dead, with fear. And he went unconscious.

When he opened his eyes again he started, seeing something creeping swiftly up a tree trunk. It was a little bird. And the bird was whistling overhead. Tap-tap-tap – it was the small, quick bird rapping the tree trunk with its beak, as if its head were a little round hammer. He watched it curiously. It shifted sharply, in its creeping fashion. Then, like a mouse, it slid down the bare trunk. Its swift creeping sent a flash of revulsion through him. He raised his head. It felt a great weight. Then, the little bird ran out of the shadow across a still patch of sunshine, its little head bobbing swiftly, its white legs twinkling brightly for a moment. How neat it was in its build, so compact, with pieces of white on its wings. There were several of them.

They were so pretty – but they crept like swift, erratic mice, running here and there among the beech-mast.

He lay down again exhausted, and his consciousness lapsed. He had a horror of the little creeping birds. All his blood seemed to be darting and creeping in his head. And yet he could not move.

He came to with a further ache of exhaustion. There was the pain in his head, and the horrible sickness, and his inability to move. He had never been ill in his life. He did not know where he was or what he was. Probably he had got sunstroke. Or what else? – he had silenced the Captain for ever – some time ago – oh, a long time ago. There had been blood on his face, and his eyes had turned upwards. It was all right, some-how. It was peace. But now he had got beyond himself. He had never been here before. Was it life, or not life? He was by himself. They were in a big, bright place, those others, and he was outside. The town, all the country, a big bright place of light: and he was outside, here, in the darkened open beyond, where each thing existed alone. But they would all have to come out there sometime, those others. Little, and left behind him, they all were. There had been father and mother and sweetheart. What did they all matter? This was the open land.

He sat up. Something scuffled. It was a little brown squirrel running in lovely undulating bounds over the floor, its red tail completing the undulation of its body – and then, as it sat up, furling and unfurling. He watched it, pleased. It ran on again, friskily, enjoying itself. It flew wildly at another squirrel, and they were chasing each other, and making little scolding, chattering noises. The soldier wanted to speak to them. But only a hoarse sound came out of his throat. The squirrels burst away – they flew up the trees. And then he saw the one peeping round at him, half-way up a tree-trunk. A start of fear went through him, though in so far as he was conscious, he was amused. It still stayed, its little keen face staring at him half-way up the tree trunk, its little ears pricked up, its clawey little hands clinging to the bark, its white breast reared. He started from it in panic.

Struggling to his feet, he lurched away. He went on walking, walking, looking for something – for a drink. His brain felt hot and inflamed for want of water. He stumbled on. Then he did not know anything. He went unconscious as he walked. Yet he stumbled on, his mouth open.

When, to his dumb wonder, he opened his eyes on the world again, he no longer tried to remember what it was. There was thick, golden light behind golden-green glitterings, and tall, grey-purple shafts, and darknesses farther off, surrounding him, growing deeper. He was conscious of a sense of arrival. He was amid the reality, on the real, dark bottom. But there was the thirst burning in his brain. He felt lighter, not so heavy. He supposed it was newness. The air was muttering with thunder. He thought he was walking wonderfully swiftly and was coming straight to relief – or was it to water?

Suddenly he stood still with fear. There was a tremendous flare of gold, immense – just a few dark trunks like bars between him and it. All the young level wheat was burnished gold glaring on its silky green. A woman, full-skirted, a black cloth on her head for head-dress, was passing like a block of shadow through the glistening, green corn, into the full glare. There was a farm, too, pale blue in shadow, and the timber black. And there was a church spire, nearly fused away in the gold. The woman moved on, away from him. He had no language with which to speak to her. She was the bright, solid unreality. She would make a noise of words that would confuse him, and her eyes would look at him without seeing him. She was crossing there to the other side. He stood against a tree.

When at last he turned, looking down the long, bare grove whose flat bed was already filling dark, he saw the mountains in a wonder-light, not far away, and radiant. Behind the soft, grey ridge of the nearest range the farther mountains stood golden and pale grey, the snow all radiant like pure, soft gold. So still, gleaming in the sky, fashioned pure out of the ore of the sky, they shone in their silence. He stood and looked at them, his face illuminated. And like the golden, lustrous gleaming of the snow he felt his own thirst bright in him. He stood and gazed, leaning against a tree. And then everything slid away into space.

During the night the lightning fluttered perpetually, making the whole sky white. He must have walked again. The world hung livid round him for moments, fields a level sheen of grey-green light, trees in dark bulk, and the range of clouds black across a white sky. Then the darkness fell like a shutter, and the night was whole. A faint flutter of a half-revealed world, that could not quite leap out of the darkness! – Then there again stood a sweep of pallor for the land, dark shapes looming, a range of clouds hanging overhead. The world was a ghostly shadow, thrown for a moment upon the pure darkness, which returned ever whole and complete.

And the mere delirium of sickness and fever went on inside him – his brain opening and shutting like the night – then sometimes convulsions of terror from something with great eyes that stared round a tree – then the long agony of the march, and the sun decomposing his blood – then the pang of hate for the Captain, followed by a pang of tenderness and ease. But everything was distorted, born of an ache and resolving into an ache.

In the morning he came definitely awake. Then his brain flamed with the sole horror of thirstiness! The sun was on his face, the dew was steaming from his wet clothes. Like one possessed, he got up. There, straight in front of him, blue and cool and tender, the mountains ranged across the pale edge of the morning sky. He wanted them – he wanted them alone – he wanted to leave himself and be identified with them. They did not move, they were still and soft, with white, gentle markings of snow. He stood still, mad with suffering, his hands crisping and clutching. Then he was twisting in a paroxysm on the grass.

He lay still, in a kind of dream of anguish. His thirst seemed to have separated itself from him, and to stand apart, a single demand. Then the pain he felt was another single self. Then there was the clog of his body, another separate thing. He was divided among all kinds of separate things. There was some strange, agonised connection between them, but they were drawing farther apart. Then they would all split. The sun, drilling down on him, was drilling through the bond. Then they would all fall, fall through the everlasting lapse of space. Then again, his consciousness reasserted itself. He roused on to his elbow and stared at the gleaming mountains. There they ranked, all still and wonderful between earth and heaven. He stared till his eyes went black, and the mountains, as they stood in their beauty, so clean and cool, seemed to have it, that which was lost in him.

IV

When the soldiers found him, three hours later, he was lying with his face over his arm, his black hair giving off heat under the sun. But he was still alive. Seeing the open, black mouth the young soldiers dropped him in horror.

He died in the hospital at night, without having seen again.

The doctors saw the bruises on his legs, behind, and were silent.

The bodies of the two men lay together, side by side, in the mortuary, the one white and slender, but laid rigidly at rest, the other looking as if every moment it must rouse into life again, so young and unused, from a slumber.

# A Sequence of Nature Poems

### A Doe at Evening

As I went through the marshes
a doe sprang out of the corn
and flashed up the hill-side
leaving her fawn.

On the sky-line
she moved round to watch,
she pricked a fine black blotch
on the sky.

I looked at her
and felt her watching;
I became a strange being.
Still, I had my right to be there with her.

Her nimble shadow trotting
along the sky-line, she
put back her fine, level-balanced head.
And I knew her.

Ah yes, being male, is not my head hard-balanced, antlered?
Are not my haunches light?
Has she not fled on the same wind with me?
Does not my fear cover her fear?

*Irschenhausen*

### Bare Almond-trees

Wet almond-trees, in the rain,
Like iron sticking grimly out of earth;
Black almond trunks, in the rain,
Like iron implements twisted, hideous, out of the earth,
Out of the deep, soft fledge of Sicilian winter-green,

Earth-grass uneatable,
Almond trunks curving blackly, iron-dark, climbing the slopes.

Almond-tree, beneath the terrace rail,
Black, rusted, iron trunk,
You have welded your thin stems finer,
Like steel, like sensitive steel in the air,
Grey, lavender, sensitive steel, curving thinly and brittly up in a
    parabola.

What are you doing in the December rain?
Have you a strange electric sensitiveness in your steel tips?
Do you feel the air for electric influences
Like some strange magnetic apparatus?
Do you take in messages, in some strange code,
From heaven's wolfish, wandering electricity, that prowls so
    constantly round Etna?[1]
Do you take the whisper of sulphur from the air?
Do you hear the chemical accents of the sun?
Do you telephone the roar of the waters over the earth?
And from all this, do you make calculations?

Sicily, December's Sicily in a mass of rain
With iron branching blackly, rusted like old, twisted
    implements
And brandishing and stooping over earth's wintry fledge,
    climbing the slopes
Of uneatable soft green!

*Taormina*

## THE BLUE JAY

The blue jay with a crest on his head
Comes round the cabin in the snow.
He runs in the snow like a bit of blue metal,
Turning his back on everything.

From the pine-tree that towers and hisses like a pillar of
    shaggy cloud
Immense above the cabin

[1] Sicily's mountain volcano

71

Comes a strident laugh as we approach, this little black dog
    and I.
So halts the little black bitch on four spread paws in the snow
And looks up inquiringly into the pillar of cloud,
With a tinge of misgiving.
*Ca-a-a!* comes the scrape of ridicule out of the tree.

*What voice of the Lord is that, from the tree of smoke?*
Oh, Bibbles, little black bitch in the snow,
With a pinch of snow in the groove of your silly snub nose,
What do you look at *me* for?
What do you look at me for, with such misgiving?

It's the blue jay laughing at us.
It's the blue jay jeering at us, Bibs.

Every day since the snow is here
The blue jay paces round the cabin, very busy, picking up bits,
Turning his back on us all,
And bobbing his thick dark crest about the snow, as if darkly
    saying:
*I ignore those folk who look out.*
You acid-blue metallic bird,
You thick bird with a strong crest,
Who are you?
Whose boss are you, with all your bully way?
You copper-sulphate blue bird!

*Lobo*

## Mountain Lion

Climbing through the January snow, into the Lobo canyon
Dark grow the spruce-trees, blue is the balsam, water
    sounds still unfrozen, and the trail is still evident.

Men!
Two men!
Men! The only animal in the world to fear!

They hesitate.
We hesitate.
They have a gun.
We have no gun.

Then we all advance, to meet.

Two Mexicans, strangers, emerging out of the dark and
    snow and inwardness of the Lobo valley.
What are they doing here on this vanishing trail?

What is he carrying?
Something yellow.
A deer?

*Qué tiene, amigo?*[1]
*León*[2] –

He smiles, foolishly, as if he were caught doing wrong.
And we smile, foolishly, as if we didn't know.
He is quite gentle and dark-faced.

It is a mountain lion,
A long, long slim cat, yellow like a lioness.
Dead.

He trapped her this morning, he says, smiling foolishly.

Lift up her face,
Her round, bright face, bright as frost.
Her round, fine-fashioned head, with two dead ears;
And stripes in the brilliant frost of her face, sharp, fine
    dark rays,
Dark, keen, fine rays in the brilliant frost of her face.
Beautiful dead eyes.

*Hermoso es!*[3]

They go out towards the open;
We go on into the gloom of Lobo.
And above the trees I found her lair,
A hole in the blood-orange brilliant rocks that stick up, a
    little cave.
And bones, and twigs, and a perilous ascent.

[1] (Spanish) What are you carrying, friend?
[2] Lion
[3] How beautiful it is! (Spanish)

So, she will never leap up that way again, with the yellow
    flash of a mountain lion's long shoot!
And her bright striped frost-face will never watch any more,
    out of the shadow of the cave in the blood-orange rock,
Above the trees of the Lobo dark valley-mouth!

Instead, I look out.
And out to the dim of the desert, like a dream, never real;
To the snow of the Sangre de Cristo mountains,[1] the ice of the
    mountains of Picoris,
And near across at the opposite steep of snow, green trees
    motionless standing in snow, like a Christmas toy.

And I think in this empty world there was room for me and
    a mountain lion.
And I think in the world beyond, how easily we might spare
    a million or two of humans
And never miss them.
Yet what a gap in the world, the missing white frost-face of
    that slim yellow mountain lion!

*Lobo*

---

[1] (lit.) Blood of Christ mountains: a range of mountains in New Mexico which
stretches into Colorado

# A Night at Mandas

from *Sea and Sardinia*

It was not much after seven when we came to Mandas. Mandas is a junction where these little trains sit and have a long happy chat after their arduous scramble over the downs. It has taken us somewhere about five hours to do our fifty miles. No wonder then that when the junction at last heaves in sight everybody bursts out of the train like seeds from an exploding pod, and rushes somewhere for something. To the station restaurant, of course. Hence there is a little station restaurant that does a brisk trade, and where one can have a bed.

A quite pleasant woman behind the little bar: a brown woman with brown parted hair and brownish eyes and brownish, tanned complexion and tight brown velveteen bodice. She led us up a narrow winding stone stair, as up a fortress, leading on with her candle, and ushered us into the bedroom. It smelled horrid and sourish, as shut-up bedrooms do. We threw open the window. There were big frosty stars snapping ferociously in heaven.

The room contained a huge bed, big enough for eight people, and quite clean. And the table on which stood the candle actually had a cloth. But imagine that cloth! I think it had been originally white: now, however, it was such a web of time-eaten holes and mournful black ink stains and poor dead wine stains that it was like some 2000 B.C. mummy-cloth. I wonder if it could have been lifted from that table: or if it was mummified on to it! I for one made no attempt to try. But that table cover impressed me, as showing degrees I had not imagined – a tablecloth.

We went down the fortress-stair to the eating-room. Here was a long table with soup plates upside down and a lamp burning an uncanny naked acetylene flame. We sat at the cold table, and the lamp immediately began to wane. The room – in fact the whole of Sardinia – was stone cold, stone, stone cold. Outside the earth was freezing. Inside there was no thought of any sort of warmth: dungeon stone floors, dungeon stone walls, and a dead, corpse-like atmosphere, too heavy and icy to move.

The lamp went quite out, and the q-b[1] gave a cry. The brown woman poked her head through a hole in the wall. Beyond her we saw the flames of the cooking, and two devil-figures stirring the pots. The brown woman came and shook the lamp – it was like a stodgy porcelain mantlepiece vase – shook it well and stirred up its innards, and started it going once more. Then she appeared with a bowl of smoking cabbage soup, in which were bits of macaroni: and would we have wine? I shuddered at the thought of death-cold red wine of the country, so asked what else there was. There was malvagia – malvoisie, the same old malmsey[2] that did for the Duke of Clarence. So we had a pint of malvagia, and were comforted. At least we were being so – when the lamp went out again. The brown woman came and shook and smacked it, and started it off again. But as if to say "Shan't for you," it whipped out again.

Then came the host with a candle and a pin, a large, genial Sicilian with pendulous moustaches. And he thoroughly pricked the wretch with the pin, shook it, and turned little screws. So up flared the flame. We were a little nervous. He asked us where we came from, etc. And suddenly he asked us, with an excited gleam, were we Socialists. Aha, he was going to hail us as citizens and comrades. He thought we were a pair of Bolshevist[3] agents: I could see it. And as such he was prepared to embrace us. But no, the q-b disclaimed the honour. I merely smiled and shook my head. It is a pity to rob people of their exciting illusions.

"Ah, there is too much Socialism everywhere!" cried the q-b.

"Ma – perhaps, perhaps –" said the discreet Sicilian. She saw which way the land lay, and added:

"*Si vuole un* pochettino *di socialismo*: one wants a tiny bit of Socialism in the world, a tiny bit. But not much. Not much. At present there is too much."

Our host, twinkling at this speech which treated of the sacred creed as if it were a pinch of salt in the broth, believing the q-b was throwing dust in his eyes, and thoroughly intrigued by us as a pair of deep ones, retired. No sooner had he gone than the lamp flame stood up at its full length, and started to whistle.

[1] short for "queen-bee" – "the q-b" is Frieda Lawrence
[2] a strong sweet wine
[3] Russian Socialist extremists – later called Communists

The q-b drew back. Not satisfied by this, another flame suddenly began to whip round the bottom of the burner, like a lion lashing its tail. Unnerved, we made room: the q-b cried again: in came the host with a subtle smile and a pin and an air of benevolence, and tamed the brute.

What else was there to eat? There was a piece of fried pork for me, and boiled eggs for the q-b. As we were proceeding with these, in came the remainder of the night's entertainment: three station officials, two in scarlet peaked caps, one in a black and gold peaked cap. They sat down with a clamour, in their caps, as if there was a sort of invisible screen between us and them. They were young. The black-cap had a lean and sardonic look: one of the red-caps was little and ruddy, very young, with a little moustache: we called him the *maialino*, the gay little black pig, he was so plump and food-nourished and frisky. The third was rather puffy and pale and had spectacles. They all seemed to present us the blank side of their cheek, and to intimate that no, they were not going to take their hats off, even if it were dinner-table and a strange *signora*. And they made rough quips with one another, still as if we were on the other side of the invisible screen.

Determined however to remove this invisible screen, I said good evening, and it was very cold. They muttered good evening, and yes, it was fresh. An Italian never says it is cold: it is never more than *fresco*.[1] But this hint that it was cold they took as a hint at their caps, and they became very silent, till the woman came in with the soup-bowl. Then they clamoured at her, particularly the *maialino*, what was there to eat. She told them – beefsteaks of pork. Whereat they pulled faces. Or bits of boiled pork. They sighed, looked gloomy, cheered up, and said beefsteaks, then.

And they fell on their soup. And never, from among the steam, have I heard a more joyful trio of soup-swilkering. They sucked it in from their spoons with long gusto-rich sucks. The *maialino* was the treble – he trilled his soup into his mouth with a swift sucking vibration, interrupted by bits of cabbage, which made the lamp start to dither again. Black-cap was the baritone; good, rolling spoon-sucks. And the one in spectacles was the bass: he gave sudden deep gulps. All was led by the long trilling of the *maialino*. Then suddenly, to vary matters, he cocked

[1] cool, moderately cold

up his spoon in one hand, chewed a huge mouthful of bread, and swallowed it down with a smack-smack-smack! of his tongue against his palate. As children we used to call this "clapping."

"Mother, she's clapping!" I would yell with anger, against my sister. The German word is *schmatzen*.[1]

So the *maialino* clapped like a pair of cymbals, while baritone and bass rolled on. Then in chimed the swift bright treble.

At this rate, however, the soup did not last long. Arrived the beefsteaks of pork. And now the trio was a trio of castanet smacks and cymbal claps. Triumphantly the *maialino* looked round. He out-smacked all.

The bread of the country is rather coarse and brown, with a hard, hard crust. A large rock of this is perched on every damp serviette. The *maialino* tore his rock asunder, and grumbled at the black-cap, who had got a weird sort of three-cornered loaf-roll of pure white bread – starch white. He was a swell with this white bread.

Suddenly black-cap turned to me. Where had we come from, where were we going, what for? But in laconic, sardonic tone.

"I *like* Sardinia," cried the q-b.

"Why?" he asked sarcastically. And she tried to find out.

"Yes, the Sardinians please me more than the Sicilians," said I.

"Why?" he asked sarcastically.

"They are more open – more honest." He seemed to turn his nose down.

"The *padrone*[2] is a Sicilian," said the *maialino*, stuffing a huge block of bread into his mouth, and rolling his insouciant eyes of a gay, well-fed little black pig towards the background. We weren't making much headway.

"You've seen Cagliari?"[3] the black-cap said to me, like a threat.

"Yes! oh, Cagliari pleases me – Cagliari is beautiful!" cried the q-b, who travels with a vial of melted butter ready for her parsnips.

"Yes – Cagliari is *so-so* – Cagliari is very fair," said the black-cap. "*Cagliari è discreta*."[4] He was evidently proud of it.

---

[1] smacking (of the lips)
[2] proprietor
[3] a town in Sardinia
[4] Cagliari is not bad

"And is Mandas nice?" asked the q-b.

"In what way nice?" they asked, with immense sarcasm.

"Is there anything to see?"

"Hens," said the *maialino* briefly. They all bristled when one asked if Mandas was nice.

"What does one do here?" asked the q-b.

"*Niente!* At Mandas one does *nothing*. At Mandas one goes to bed when it's dark, like a chicken. At Mandas one walks down the road like a pig that is going nowhere. At Mandas a goat understands more than the inhabitants understand. At Mandas one needs socialism. . . ."

They all cried out at once. Evidently Mandas was more than flesh and blood could bear for another minute to these three conspirators.

"Then you are very bored here?" say I.

"Yes."

And the quiet intensity of that naked *yes* spoke more than volumes.

"You would like to be in Cagliari?"

"Yes."

Silence, intense, sardonic silence had intervened. The three looked at one another and made a sour joke about Mandas. Then the black-cap turned to me.

"Can you understand Sardinian?" he said.

"Somewhat. More than Sicilian, anyhow."

"But Sardinian is more difficult than Sicilian. It is full of words utterly unknown to Italian –"

"Yes, but," say I, "it is spoken openly, in plain words, and Sicilian is spoken all stuck together, none of the words there at all."

He looks at me as if I were an impostor. Yet it is true. I find it quite easy to understand Sardinian. As a matter of fact, it is more a question of human approach than of sound. Sardinian seems open and manly and downright. Sicilian is gluey and evasive, as if the Sicilian didn't want to speak straight to you. As a matter of fact, he doesn't. He is an over-cultured, sensitive, ancient soul, and he has so many sides to his mind that he hasn't got any definite one mind at all. He's got a dozen minds, and uneasily he's aware of it, and to commit himself to any one of them is merely playing a trick on himself and his interlocutor. The Sardinian, on the other hand, still seems to have one downright mind. I bump up against a downright, smack-out belief in socialism, for example. The Sicilian is much too old in our culture to swallow socialism whole: much too ancient and *rusé*[1] not to be sophisticated about any and every belief. He'll go off like a squib: and then he'll smoulder acridly and sceptically even against his own fire. One sympathizes with him in retrospect. But in daily life it is unbearable.

"Where do you find such white bread?" say I to the black-cap, because he is proud of it.

"It comes from my home." And then he asks about the bread of Sicily. Is it any whiter than *this* – the Mandas rock? Yes, it is a little whiter. At which they gloom again. For it is a very sore point, this bread. Bread means a great deal to an Italian: it is verily his staff of life. He practically lives on bread. And instead of going by taste, he now, like all the world, goes by eye. He has got it into his head that bread should be white, so that every time he fancies a darker shade in the loaf a shadow falls on his soul. Nor is he altogether wrong. For although, personally, I don't like white bread any more, yet I do like my brown bread to be made of pure, unmixed flour. The peasants in Sicily, who have kept their own wheat and make their own natural brown bread, ah, it is amazing how fresh and sweet and *clean* their loaf seems, so perfumed, as home-bread used all to be before the war. Whereas the bread of the commune, the regulation supply, is hard, and rather coarse and rough, so rough and harsh on the palate. One gets tired to death of it. I suspect myself the maize meal mixed in. But I don't know. And finally the bread varies immensely from town to town, from commune to commune. The so-called just and equal distribution is all-my-eye. One place has abundance of good sweet bread, another scrapes along, always stinted, on an allowance of harsh coarse stuff. And the poor suffer bitterly, really, from the bread-stinting, because they depend so on this one food. They say the inequality and the injustice of distribution come from the Camorra[2] – la grande Camorra – which is no more nowadays than a profiteering combine, which the poor hate. But for myself, I don't know. I only know that one town – Venice, for example – seems to have an endless supply of pure bread, of sugar, of tobacco, of salt – while Florence is in one continual ferment of irritation over

[1] artful
[2] a rogues' secret society associated with rackets and swindles

the stinting of these supplies – which are all Government monopolies, doled out accordingly.

We said good night to our three railway friends, and went up to bed. We had only been in the room a minute or two, when the brown woman tapped: and if you please, the black-cap had sent us one of his little white loaves. We were really touched. Such delicate little generosities have almost disappeared from the world.

It was a queer little bread – three-cornered, and almost as hard as ship's biscuit, made of starch flour. Not strictly bread at all.

The night was cold, the blankets flat and heavy, but one slept quite well till dawn. At seven o'clock it was a clear, cold morning, the sun not yet up. Standing at the bedroom window looking out, I could hardly believe my eyes, it was so like England, like Cornwall in the bleak parts, or Derbyshire uplands. There was a little paddock-garden at the back of the station, rather tumble-down, with two sheep in it. There were several forlorn-looking outbuildings, very like Cornwall. And then the wide, forlorn country road stretched away between borders of grass and low, drystone walls,[1] towards a greystone farm with a tuft of trees, and a naked stone village in the distance. The sun came up yellow, the bleak country glimmered bluish and reluctant. The low, green hill-slopes were divided into fields, with low drystone walls and ditches. Here and there a stone barn rose alone, or with a few bare, windy trees attached. Two rough-coated winter horses pastured on the rough grass, a boy came along the naked, wide, grass-bordered high-road with a couple of milk cans, drifting in from nowhere: and it was all Cornwall, or a part of Ireland, that the old nostalgia for the Celtic regions[2] began to spring up in me. Ah, those old, drystone walls dividing the fields – pale and granite-blenched! Ah, the dark, sombre grass, the naked sky! the forlorn horses in the wintry morning! Strange is a Celtic landscape, far more moving, disturbing, than the lovely glamour of Italy and Greece. Before the curtains of history lifted, one feels the world was like this – this Celtic bareness and sombreness and *air*. But perhaps

[1] walls constructed without the use of mortar in hill country
[2] regions in which the ancient Celtic race settled – e.g. Scotland, Ireland, Wales, Cornwall, Brittany

it is not Celtic at all: Iberian.[1] Nothing is more unsatisfactory than our conception of what is Celtic and what is not Celtic. I believe there were never any Celts, as a race. – As for the Iberians – !

Wonderful to go out on a frozen road, to see the grass in shadow bluish with hoar-frost, to see the grass in the yellow winter sunrise beams melting and going cold-twinkly. Wonderful the bluish, cold air, and things standing up in cold distance. After two southern winters, with roses blooming all the time, this bleakness and this touch of frost in the ringing morning go to my soul like an intoxication. I am so glad, on this lonely naked road, I don't know what to do with myself. I walk down in the shallow grassy ditches under the loose stone walls. I walk on the little ridge of grass, the little bank on which the wall is built, I cross the road across the frozen cow-droppings: and it is all so familiar to my *feet*, my very feet in contact, that I am wild as if I had made a discovery. And I realize that I hate limestone, to live on limestone or marble or any of those limy rocks. I hate them. They are dead rocks, they have no life – thrills for the feet. Even sandstone is much better. But granite! Granite is my favourite. It is so live under the feet, it has a deep sparkle of its own. I like its roundnesses – and I hate the jaggy dryness of limestone, that burns in the sun, and withers.

After coming to a deep well in a grassy plot in a wide space of the road, I go back, across the sunny naked upland country, towards the pink station and its outbuildings. An engine is steaming its white clouds in the new light. Away to the left there is even a row of small houses, like a row of railwaymen's dwellings. Strange and familiar sight. And the station precincts are disorderly and rather dilapidated. I think of our Sicilian host.

The brown woman gives us coffee, and very strong, rich goat's milk, and bread. After which the q-b and I set off once more along the road to the village. She, too, is thrilled. She, too, breathes deep. She, too, feels *space* around her, and freedom to move the limbs: such as one does not feel in Italy and Sicily, where all is so classic and fixed.

[1] the Iberian peoples settled in the Iberian peninsula – i.e. what is now Spain and Portugal

The village itself is just a long, winding, darkish street, in shadow, of houses and shops and a smithy. It might almost be Cornwall: not quite. Something, I don't know what, suggests the stark burning glare of summer. And then, of course, there is none of the cosiness which climbing roses and lilac trees and cottage shops and haystacks would give to an English scene. This is harder, barer, starker, more dreary. An ancient man in the black and white costume comes out of a hovel of a cottage. The butcher carries a huge side of meat. The women peer at us – but more furtive and reticent than the howling stares of Italy.

So we go on, down the rough cobbled street through the whole length of the village. And emerging on the other side, past the last cottage, we find ourselves again facing the open country, on the gentle down-slope of the rolling hill. The landscape continues the same: low, rolling upland hills, dim under the yellow sun of the January morning: stone fences, fields, grey arable land: a man slowly, slowly ploughing with a pony and a dark red cow: the road trailing empty across the distance: and then, the one violently unfamiliar note, the enclosed cemetery lying outside on the gentle hillside, closed in all round, very compact, with high walls: and on the inside face of the enclosure wall the marble slabs, like shut drawers of the sepulchres, shining white, the wall being like a chest of drawers, or pigeon-holes to hold the dead. Tufts of dark and plumy cypresses rise among the flat graves of the enclosure. In the south, cemeteries are walled off and isolated very tight. The dead, as it were, are kept fast in pound. There is no spreading of graves over the face of the country. They are penned in a tight fold, with cypresses to fatten on the bones. This is the one thoroughly strange note in the landscape. But all-pervading there is a strangeness, that strange feeling as if the *depths* were barren, which comes in the south and the east, sun-stricken. Sun-stricken, and the heart eaten out by the dryness.

"I like it! I like it!" cries the q-b.

"But could you live here?" She would like to say yes, but daren't.

We stray back. The q-b wants to buy one of those saddle-bag arrangements. I say what for? She says to keep things in. Ach! but peeping in the shops, we see one and go in and examine it. It is quite a sound one, properly made: but plain, quite plain. On the white cross-stripes there are no lovely coloured flowers of rose and green and magenta: the three favourite Sardinian colours: nor are there any of the fantastic, griffin-like beasts. So it won't do. How much does it cost? Forty-five francs.

There is nothing to do in Mandas. So we will take the morning train and go to the terminus, to Sorgono. Thus, we shall cross the lower slopes of the great central knot of Sardinia, the mountain knot called Gennargentu. And Sorgono we feel will be lovely.

Back at the station we make tea on the spirit lamp, fill the thermos, pack the knapsack, and the kitchenino, and come out into the sun of the platform. The q-b goes to thank the black-cap for the white bread, whilst I settle the bill and ask for food for the journey. The brown woman fishes out from a huge black pot in the background sundry hunks of coarse boiled pork, and gives me two of these, hot, with bread and salt. This is the luncheon. I pay the bill: which amounts to twenty-four francs, for everything. (One says francs or liras, irrespective, in Italy.) At that moment arrives the train from Cagliari, and men rush in, roaring for the soup – or, rather, for the broth. "Ready, ready!" she cries, going to the black pot.

# A Letter from Italy

*Lerici, per Fiascherino,*
*Golfo della Spezia, Italia.*

18 *Dec.*, 1913

DEAR WILL, –

I *was* glad to get that letter from you, full of good old crusty Eastwood gossip. Always write to me like that.

And don't wonder at what I write now, for Felice is rattling away like a hail-storm in Italian, just near my left ear, and Frieda, with her usual softness of heart (and head now and then), is letting herself in for things that will need the courage of St George to extricate her from.

We *have* got a beautiful place here (and don't lose the address). It is a little pink cottage of four rooms, under great hills of olive woods, just over the sea. We have a great vine garden, all shut in, and lemons on the wall, and today, with a wind from the Apennines, the big, heavy oranges swing gold in their dark green leaves. We've only one orange tree, but it is a beauty.

There is no road here, that carts may pass – not even a mule road. Everything must go by rowing boat on the sea, that is not carried on the heads of the peasants. They carry, women and all, masses of stuff on their heads. It is supposed to give them a beautiful carriage, but that is a lie. It presses in the loins in a most curious fashion.

At this time of the year all the women are out in the olive woods – you have no idea how beautiful olives are, so grey, so delicately sad, reminding one constantly of the New Testament. I am always expecting when I go to Tellaro for the letters, to meet Jesus gossiping with his disciples as he goes along above the sea, under the grey, light trees. Now the hills are full of voices, the peasant women and children all day long and day after day, in the faint shadow of olives, picking the fallen fruit off the ground, pannier after pannier full. Our village is Tellaro.

It grows sheer out of the rocks of the sea, a searobber's nest of 200 souls. The church is over the water. There is a tale that once in the night the church bell rang, and rang again. The people got up in terror – the bell rang mysteriously. Then it was found that the bell rope had fallen over the edge of the cliff in among the rocks, and an octopus had got hold of the end, and was drawing it. It is quite possible. The men go fishing for the octopus with a white bait and a long spear. They get quite big ones, six or seven pounds in weight sometimes – and you never saw anything so fiendishly ugly. But they are good to eat. We were at a peasant wedding the other day, and a great feast – octopus was one of the dishes: but I could not fancy it: I can eat snails all right, but octopus – no. We can have the boat belonging to the peasants on the bay when we like, and row out on the sea. The Mediterranean is quite wonderful – and when the sun sets beyond the islands of Porto Venere, and all the sea is like heaving white milk with a street of fire across it, and amethyst islands away back, it is too beautiful.

I am very fond of the Italians. We have a little oddity of a maid called Elide – 25 years old. Her old mother Felice is quite a figure. They are very funny and ceremonious. When Elide has put the soup on the table, she says "*a rivederci*,[1] eh?" before she can leave us. There is only one other house on this bay – only one other house within nearly a mile – and that is the peasants' down on the beach. They are cousins of Elide. Sometimes they come and play and sing with us at evening – bringing the guitar. It is jolly. Luigi is very beautiful – and Gentile is a wild joy. How happy you would be with these people – and Mrs Hopkin with the country. The wind is now cold – there is snow on the mountains over Carrara – but still at night a glow-worm shines near the door, and sometimes a butterfly, a big black and red one, wanders to the remaining flowers – wild pinks and campanulas. I love living by the sea – one gets so used to its noise, one hears it no more. And the ships that pass, with many sails, to Sardinia and Sicily, and through the gates of Porto Venere to Genova, are very beautiful. Spezia is Italy's great naval arsenal. Right in the harbour lie her warships: and she wastes such a lot of powder with their rattling cannon. The men of the villages go into Spezia to work. The

[1]goodbye. See you again soon.

workmen run the only steamers across the bay. They are interesting.

And now, after all this, you must come – you and Mrs Hopkin at least – and Enid if she can. You can get here cheap, some way or other – perhaps by sea to Genoa or to Leghorn – or by trips. We shall be here, I think, till June. So make up your minds, and scrape together. I want you. We both *want* you to come – and it is the most beautiful place I know.

I am laughing at your swatting with Willie Dunn. We send heaps of good wishes for Christmas. Write to me oftener. And make up your minds to come. Mrs Hopkin promised us last spring.

Love from Frieda and me to you three.

Yrs,

D. H. LAWRENCE

One of Lawrence's water-colour paintings, entitled *Italian Scene with Boat*, probably composed during his visit to Italy with Frieda in 1913.

# Samson and Delilah

A man got down from the motor-omnibus that runs from Penzance to St Just-in-Penwith,[1] and turned northwards, uphill towards the Polestar. It was only half past six, but already the stars were out, a cold little wind was blowing from the sea, and the crystalline, three-pulse flash of the lighthouse below the cliffs beat rhythmically in the first darkness.

The man was alone. He went his way unhesitating, but looked from side to side with cautious curiosity. Tall, ruined power-houses of tin-mines[2] loomed in the darkness from time to time, like remnants of some by-gone civilization. The lights of many miners' cottages scattered on the hilly darkness twinkled desolate in their disorder, yet twinkled with the lonely homeliness of the Celtic[3] night.

He tramped steadily on, always watchful with curiosity. He was a tall, well-built man, apparently in the prime of life. His shoulders were square and rather stiff, he leaned forwards a little as he went, from the hips, like a man who must stoop to lower his height. But he did not stoop his shoulders: he bent his straight back from the hips.

Now and again short, stump, thick-legged figures of Cornish miners passed him, and he invariably gave them goodnight, as if to insist that he was on his own ground. He spoke with the west-Cornish intonation. And as he went along the dreary road, looking now at the lights of the dwellings on land, now at the lights away to sea, vessels veering round in sight of the Longships Lighthouse, the whole of the Atlantic Ocean in darkness and space between him and America, he seemed a little excited and pleased with himself, watchful, thrilled, veering along in a sense of mastery and of power in conflict.

The houses began to close on the road, he was entering the straggling, formless, desolate mining village, that he knew of

[1] West Penwith is the Cornish name for the Land's End peninsula. St Just is a
   large village close to the north coast, a few miles from Land's End
[2] typical features of the area. Some are now being worked again
[3] see note at foot of page 81

old. On the left was a little space set back from the road, and cosy lights of an inn. There it was. He peered up at the sign: "The Tinners' Rest". But he could not make out the name of the proprietor. He listened. There was excited talking and laughing, a woman's voice laughing shrilly among the men's.

Stooping a little, he entered the warmly-lit bar. The lamp was burning, a buxom woman rose from the white-scrubbed deal table where the black and white and red cards were scattered, and several men, miners, lifted their faces from the game.

The stranger went to the counter, averting his face. His cap was pulled down over his brow.

"Good-evening!" said the landlady, in her rather ingratiating voice.

"Good-evening. A glass of ale."

"A glass of ale," repeated the landlady suavely. "Cold night – but bright."

"Yes," the man assented, laconically. Then he added, when nobody expected him to say any more: "Seasonable weather."

"Quite seasonable, quite," said the landlady. "Thank you."

The man lifted his glass straight to his lips, and emptied it. He put it down again on the zinc counter with a click.

"Let's have another," he said.

The woman drew the beer, and the man went away with his glass to the second table, near the fire. The woman, after a moment's hesitation, took her seat again at the table with the card-players. She had noticed the man: a big fine fellow, well dressed, a stranger.

But he spoke with that Cornish-Yankee accent she accepted as the natural twang among the miners.

The stranger put his foot on the fender and looked into the fire. He was handsome, well coloured, with well-drawn Cornish eyebrows, and the usual dark, bright, mindless Cornish eyes. He seemed abstracted in thought. Then he watched the card-party.

The woman was buxom and healthy, with dark hair and small, quick brown eyes. She was bursting with life and vigour, the energy she threw into the game of cards excited all the men, they shouted, and laughed, and the woman held her breast, shrieking with laughter.

"Oh, my, it'll be the death o' me," she panted. "Now, come on, Mr Trevorrow, play fair. Play fair, I say, or I s'll put the cards down."

"Play fair! Why who's played unfair?" ejaculated Mr Trevorrow. "Do you mean t'accuse me, as I haven't played fair, Mrs Nankervis?"

"I do. I say it, and I mean it. Haven't you got the queen of spades? Now, come on, no dodging round me. *I* know you've got that queen, as well as I know my name's Alice."

"Well – if your name's Alice, you'll have to have it –"

"Ay, now – what did I say? Did you ever see such a man? My word, but your missus must be easy took in, by the looks of things."

And off she went into peals of laughter. She was interrupted by the entrance of four men in khaki, a short, stumpy sergeant of middle age, a young corporal, and two young privates. The woman leaned back in her chair.

"Oh, my!" she cried. "If there isn't the boys back: looking perished, I believe –"

"Perished, Ma!" exclaimed the sergeant. "Not yet."

"Near enough," said a young private, uncouthly.

The woman got up.

"I'm sure you are, my dears. You'll be wanting your suppers, I'll be bound."

"We could do with 'em."

"Let's have a wet first," said the sergeant.

The woman bustled about getting the drinks. The soldiers moved to the fire, spreading out their hands.

"Have your suppers in here, will you?" she said. "Or in the kitchen?"

"Let's have it here," said the sergeant. "More cosier – *if* you don't mind."

"You shall have it where you like, boys, where you like."

She disappeared. In a minute a girl of about sixteen came in. She was tall and fresh, with dark, young, expressionless eyes, and well-drawn brows, and the immature softness and mindlessness of the sensuous Celtic type.

"Ho, Maryann! Evenin', Maryann! How's Maryann, now?" came the multiple greeting.

She replied to everybody in a soft voice, a strange, soft *aplomb* that was very attractive. And she moved round with rather mechanical, attractive movements, as if her thoughts were elsewhere. But she had always this dim far-awayness in her bearing: a sort of modesty. The strange man by the fire watched her curiously. There was an alert, inquisitive, mindless curiosity on his well-coloured face.

"I'll have a bit of supper with you, if I might," he said.

She looked at him, with her clear, unreasoning eyes, just like the eyes of some non-human creature.

"I'll ask mother," she said. Her voice was soft-breathing, gently singsong.

When she came in again:

"Yes," she said, almost whispering. "What will you have?"

"What have you got?" he said, looking up into her face.

"There's cold meat —"

"That's for me, then."

The stranger sat at the end of the table and ate with the tired, quiet soldiers. Now, the landlady was interested in him. Her brow was knit rather tense, there was a look of panic in her large, healthy face, but her small brown eyes were fixed most dangerously. She was a big woman, but her eyes were small and tense. She drew near the stranger. She wore a rather loud-patterned flannelette blouse, and a dark skirt.

"What will you have to drink with your supper?" she asked, and there was a new, dangerous note in her voice.

He moved uneasily.

"Oh, I'll go on with ale."

She drew him another glass. Then she sat down on the bench at the table with him and the soldiers, and fixed him with her attention.

"You've come from St Just, have you?" she said.

He looked at her with those clear, dark, inscrutable Cornish eyes, and answered at length:

"No, from Penzance."

"Penzance! — but you're not thinking of going back there tonight?"

"No — no."

He still looked at her with those wide, clear eyes that seemed like very bright agate. Her anger began to rise. It was seen on her brow. Yet her voice was still suave and deprecating.

"*I thought* not — but you're not living in these parts, are you?"

"No — no, I'm not living here." He was always slow in answering, as if something intervened between him and any outside question.

"Oh, I see," she said. "You've got relations down here."

Again he looked straight into her eyes, as if looking her into silence.

"Yes," he said.

He did not say any more. She rose with a flounce. The anger was tight on her brow. There was no more laughing and card-playing that evening, though she kept up her motherly, suave, good-humoured way with the men. But they knew her, they were all afraid of her.

The supper was finished, the table cleared, the stranger did not go. Two of the young soldiers went off to bed, with their cheery:

"Good-night, Ma. Good-night, Maryann."

The stranger talked a little to the sergeant about the war, which was in its first year, about the new army, a fragment of which was quartered in this district, about America.

The landlady darted looks at him from her small eyes, minute by minute the electric storm welled in her bosom, as still he did not go. She was quivering with suppressed, violent passion, something frightening and abnormal. She could not sit still for a moment. Her heavy form seemed to flash with sudden, involuntary movements as the minutes passed by, and still he sat there, and the tension on her heart grew unbearable. She watched the hands of the clock move on. Three of the soldiers had gone to bed, only the crop-headed, terrier-like old sergeant remained.

The landlady sat behind the bar fidgeting spasmodically with the newspaper. She looked again at the clock. At last it was five minutes to ten.

"Gentlemen – the enemy!" she said, in her diminished, furious voice. "Time, please. Time, my dears. And good-night all!"

The men began to drop out, with a brief good-night. It was a minute to ten. The landlady rose.

"Come," she said. "I'm shutting the door."

The last of the miners passed out. She stood, stout and menacing, holding the door. Still the stranger sat on by the fire, his black overcoat opened, smoking.

"We're closed now, sir," came the perilous, narrowed voice of the landlady.

The little, dog-like, hard-headed sergeant touched the arm of the stranger.

"Closing time," he said.

The stranger turned round in his seat, and his quick-moving, dark, jewel-like eyes went from the sergeant to the landlady.

"I'm stopping here tonight," he said, in his laconic Cornish-Yankee accent.

The landlady seemed to tower. Her eyes lifted strangely, frightening.

"Oh! indeed!" she cried. "Oh, indeed! And whose orders are those, may I ask?"

He looked at her again.

"My orders," he said.

Involuntarily she shut the door, and advanced like a great, dangerous bird. Her voice rose, there was a touch of hoarseness in it.

"And what might *your* orders be, if you please?" she cried. "Who might *you* be, to give orders, in the house?"

He sat still, watching her.

"You know who I am," he said. "At least, I know who you are."

"Oh, you do? Oh, do you? And who am *I* then, if you'll be so good as to tell me?"

He stared at her with his bright, dark eyes.

"You're my Missis, you are," he said. "And you know it, as well as I do."

She started as if something had exploded in her.

Her eyes lifted and flared madly.

"*Do* I know it, indeed!" she cried. "I know no such thing! I know no such thing! Do you think a man's going to walk into this bar, and tell me off-hand I'm his Missis, and I'm going to believe him? – I say to you, whoever you may be, you're mistaken. I know myself for no Missis of yours, and I'll thank you to go out of this house, this minute, before I get those that will put you out."

The man rose to his feet, stretching his head towards her a little. He was a handsomely built Cornishman in the prime of life.

"What you say, eh? You don't know me?" he said, in his sing-song voice, emotionless, but rather smothered and pressing: it reminded one of the girl's. "I should know you anywhere, you see. I should! I shouldn't have to look twice to know you, you see. You see, now, don't you?"

The woman was baffled.

"So you may say," she replied, staccato. "So you may say. That's easy enough. My name's known, and respected, by most people for ten miles round. But I don't know *you*."

Her voice ran to sarcasm. "I can't say I know *you*. You're a *perfect* stranger to me, and I don't believe I've ever set eyes on you before tonight."

Her voice was very flexible and sarcastic.

"Yes, you have," replied the man, in his reasonable way. "Yes, you have. Your name's my name, and that girl Maryann is my girl; she's my daughter. You're my Missis right enough. As sure as I'm Willie Nankervis."

He spoke as if it were an accepted fact. His face was handsome, with a strange, watchful alertness and a fundamental fixity of intention that maddened her.

"You villain!" she cried. "You villain, to come to this house and dare to speak to me. You villain, you down-right rascal!"

He looked at her.

"Ay," he said, unmoved. "All that." He was uneasy before her. Only he was not afraid of her. There was something impenetrable about him, like his eyes, which were as bright as agate.

She towered, and drew near to him menacingly.

"You're going out of this house, aren't you?" – She stamped her foot in sudden madness. "*This minute!*"

He watched her. He knew she wanted to strike him.

"No," he said, with suppressed emphasis. "I've told you, I'm stopping here."

He was afraid of her personality, but it did not alter him. She wavered. Her small, tawny-brown eyes concentrated in a point of vivid, sightless fury, like a tiger's. The man was wincing, but he stood his ground. Then she bethought herself. She would gather her forces.

"We'll see whether you're stopping here," she said. And she turned, with a curious, frightening lifting of her eyes, and surged out of the room. The man, listening, heard her go upstairs, heard her tapping at a bedroom door, heard her saying: "Do you mind coming down a minute, boys? I want you. I'm in trouble."

The man in the bar took off his cap and his black overcoat, and threw them on the seat behind him. His black hair was short and touched with grey at the temples. He wore a well-cut, well-fitting suit of dark grey, American in style, and a turn-down collar. He looked well-to-do, a fine, solid figure of a man. The rather rigid look of the shoulders came from his having had his collar-bone twice broken in the mines.

The little terrier of a sergeant, in dirty khaki, looked at him furtively.

"She's your Missis?" he asked, jerking his head in the direction of the departed woman.

"Yes, she is," barked the man. "She's that, sure enough."

"Not seen her for a long time, haven't ye?"

"Sixteen years come March month."

"Hm!"

And the sergeant laconically resumed his smoking.

The landlady was coming back, followed by the three young soldiers, who entered rather sheepishly, in trousers and shirt and stocking-feet. The woman stood histrionically at the end of the bar, and exclaimed:

"That man refuses to leave the house, claims he's stopping the night here. You know very well I have no bed, don't you? And this house doesn't accommodate travellers. Yet he's going to stop in spite of all! But not while I've a drop of blood in my body, that I declare with my dying breath. And not if you men are worth the name of men, and will help a woman as has no one to help her."

Her eyes sparkled, her face was flushed pink. She was drawn up like an Amazon.[1]

The young soldiers did not quite know what to do. They looked at the man, they looked at the sergeant, one of them looked down and fastened his braces on the second button.

"What say, sergeant?" asked one whose face twinkled for a little devilment.

"Man says he's husband to Mrs Nankervis," said the sergeant.

"He's no husband of mine. I declare I never set eyes on him before this night. It's a dirty trick, nothing else, it's a dirty trick."

"Why, you're a liar, saying you never set eyes on me before," barked the man near the hearth. "You're married to me, and that girl Maryann you had by me – well enough you know it."

The young soldiers looked on in delight, the sergeant smoked imperturbed.

"Yes," sang the landlady, slowly shaking her head in supreme sarcasm, "it sounds very pretty, doesn't it? But you see we don't believe a word of it, and *how* are you going to prove it?" She

[1] the Amazons were a legendary race of tall, powerful female warriors

smiled nastily.

The man watched in silence for a moment, then he said: "It wants no proof."

"Oh, yes, but it does! Oh, yes, but it does, sir, it wants a lot of proving!" sang the lady's sarcasm. "We're not such gulls as all that, to swallow your words whole."

But he stood unmoved near the fire. She stood with one hand resting on the zinc-covered bar, the sergeant sat with legs crossed, smoking, on the seat halfway between them, the three young soldiers in their shirts and braces stood wavering in the gloom behind the bar. There was silence.

"Do you know anything of the whereabouts of your husband, Mrs Nankervis? Is he still living?" asked the sergeant, in his judicious fashion.

Suddenly the landlady began to cry, great scalding tears, that left the young men aghast.

"I know nothing of him," she sobbed, feeling for her pocket handkerchief. "He left me when Maryann was a baby, went mining to America, and after about six months never wrote a line nor sent me a penny bit. I can't say whether he's alive or dead, the villain. All I've heard of him's to the bad – and I've heard nothing for years an' all, now." She sobbed violently.

The golden-skinned, handsome man near the fire watched her as she wept. He was frightened, he was troubled, he was bewildered, but none of his emotions altered him underneath.

There was no sound in the room but the violent sobbing of the landlady. The men, one and all, were overcome.

"Don't you think as you'd better go, for tonight?" said the sergeant to the man, with sweet reasonableness. "You'd better leave it a bit, and arrange something between you. You can't have much claim on a woman, I should imagine, if it's how she says. And you've come down on her a bit too sudden-like."

The landlady sobbed heart-brokenly. The man watched her large breasts shaken. They seemed to cast a spell over his mind.

"How I've treated her, that's no matter," he replied, "I've come back, and I'm going to stop in my own home – for a bit, anyhow. There you've got it."

"A dirty action," said the sergeant, his face flushing dark. "A dirty action, to come, after deserting a woman for that number of years, and want to force yourself on her! A dirty action – as isn't allowed by the law."

The landlady wiped her eyes.

"Never you mind about law nor nothing," cried the man, in a strange, strong voice. "I'm not moving out of this public tonight."

The woman turned to the soldiers behind her, and said in a wheedling, sarcastic tone:

"Are we going to stand it, boys? – Are we going to be done like this, Sergeant Thomas, by a scoundrel and a bully as has led a life beyond *mention*, in those American mining-camps, and then wants to come back and make havoc of a poor woman's life and savings, after having left her with a baby in arms to struggle as best she might? It's a crying shame if nobody will stand up for me – a crying shame – !"

The soldiers and the little sergeant were bristling. The woman stooped and rummaged under the counter for a minute. Then, unseen to the man away near the fire, she threw out a plaited grass rope, such as is used for binding bales, and left it lying near the feet of the young soldiers, in the gloom at the back of the bar.

Then she rose and fronted the situation.

"Come now," she said to the man, in a reasonable, coldly-coaxing tone, "put your coat on and leave us alone. Be a man, and not worse than a brute of a German. You can get a bed easy enough in St Just, and if you've nothing to pay for it sergeant would lend you a couple of shilling. I'm sure he would."

All eyes were fixed on the man. He was looking down at the woman like a creature spell-bound or possessed by some devil's own intention.

"I've got money of my own," he said. "Don't you be frightened for your money, I've plenty of that, for the time."

"Well, then," she coaxed, in a cold, almost sneering propitiation, "put your coat on and go where you're wanted – be a *man*, not a brute of a German."

She had drawn quite near to him, in her challenging coaxing intentness. He looked down at her with his bewitched face.

"No, I shan't," he said. "I shan't do no such thing. *You'll* put me up for tonight."

"Shall I!" she cried. And suddenly she flung her arms round him, hung on to him with all her powerful weight, calling to the soldiers: "Get the rope, boys, and fasten him up. Alfred – John, quick now –"

The man reared, looked round with maddened eyes, and heaved his powerful body. But the woman was powerful also, and very heavy, and was clenched with the determination of death. Her face, with its exulting, horribly vindictive look, was turned up to him from his own breast; he reached back his head frantically, to get away from it. Meanwhile the young soldiers, after having watched this frightful Laocoon[1] swaying for a moment, stirred, and the malicious one darted swiftly with the rope. It was tangled a little.

"Give me the end here," cried the sergeant.

Meanwhile the big man heaved and struggled, swung the woman round against the seat and the table, in his convulsive effort to get free. But she pinned down his arms like a cuttlefish wreathed heavily upon him. And he heaved and swayed, and they crashed about the room, the soldiers hopping, the furniture bumping.

The young soldier had got the rope once round, the brisk sergeant helping him. The woman sank heavily lower, they got the rope round several times. In the struggle the victim fell over against the table. The ropes tightened till they cut his arms. The woman clung to his knees. Another soldier ran in a flash of genius, and fastened the strange man's feet with the pair of braces. Seats had crashed over, the table was thrown against the wall, but the man was bound, his arms pinned against his sides, his feet tied. He lay half fallen, sunk against the table, still for a moment.

The woman rose, and sank, faint, on to the seat against the wall. Her breast heaved, she could not speak, she thought she was going to die. The bound man lay against the overturned table, his coat all twisted and pulled up beneath the ropes, leaving the loins exposed. The soldiers stood around, a little dazed, but excited with the row.

The man began to struggle again, heaving instinctively against the ropes, taking great, deep breaths. His face, with its golden skin, flushed dark and surcharged, he heaved again. The great veins in his neck stood out. But it was no good, he went relaxed. Then again, suddenly, he jerked his feet.

"Another pair of braces, William," cried the excited soldier. He threw himself on the legs of the bound man, and managed to fasten the knees. Then again there was stillness. They could hear the clock tick.

The woman looked at the prostrate figure, the strong, straight

---

[1] in the Greek legend Laocoon was crushed to death by two great sea serpents

limbs, the strong back bound in subjection, the wide-eyed face that reminded her of a calf tied in a sack in a cart, only its head stretched dumbly backwards. And she triumphed.

The bound-up body began to struggle again. She watched fascinated the muscles working, the shoulders, the hips, the large, clean thighs. Even now he might break the ropes. She was afraid. But the lively young soldier sat on the shoulders of the bound man, and after a few perilous moments, there was stillness again.

"Now," said the judicious sergeant to the bound man, "if we untie you, will you promise to go off and make no more trouble."

"You'll not untie him in here," cried the woman. "I wouldn't trust him as far as I could blow him."

There was silence.

"We might carry him outside, and undo him there," said the soldier. "Then we could get the policeman, if he made any bother."

"Yes," said the sergeant. "We could do that." Then again, in an altered, almost severe tone, to the prisoner. "If we undo you outside, will you take your coat and go without creating any more disturbance?"

But the prisoner would not answer, he only lay with wide, dark, bright, eyes, like a bound animal. There was a space of perplexed silence.

"Well, then, do as you say," said the woman irritably. "Carry him out amongst you, and let us shut up the house."

They did so. Picking up the bound man, the four soldiers staggered clumsily into the silent square in front of the inn, the woman following with the cap and the overcoat. The young soldiers quickly unfastened the braces from the prisoner's legs, and they hopped indoors. They were in their stocking-feet, and outside the stars flashed cold. They stood in the doorway watching. The man lay quite still on the cold ground.

"Now," said the sergeant, in a subdued voice, "I'll loosen the knot, and he can work himself free, if you go in, Missis."

She gave a last look at the dishevelled, bound man, as he sat on the ground. Then she went indoors, followed quickly by the sergeant. Then they were heard locking and barring the door.

The man seated on the ground outside worked and strained at the rope. But it was not so easy to undo himself even now. So, with hands bound, making an effort, he got on his feet, and went and worked the cord against the rough edge of an old wall. The rope, being of a kind of plaited grass, soon frayed and broke, and he freed himself. He had various contusions. His arms were hurt and bruised from the bonds. He rubbed them slowly. Then he pulled his clothes straight, stooped, put on his cap, struggled into his overcoat, and walked away.

The stars were very brilliant. Clear as crystal, the beam from the lighthouse under the cliffs struck rhythmically on the night. Dazed, the man walked along the road past the churchyard. Then he stood leaning up against a wall, for a long time.

He was roused because his feet were so cold. So he pulled himself together, and turned again in the silent night, back towards the inn.

The bar was in darkness. But there was a light in the kitchen. He hesitated. Then very quietly he tried the door.

He was surprised to find it open. He entered, and quietly closed it behind him. Then he went down the step past the bar-counter, and through to the lighted doorway of the kitchen. There sat his wife, planted in front of the range, where a furze fire was burning. She sat in a chair full in front of the range, her knees wide apart on the fender. She looked over her shoulder at him as he entered, but she did not speak. Then she stared in the fire again.

It was a small, narrow kitchen. He dropped his cap on the table that was covered with yellowish American cloth, and took a seat with his back to the wall, near the oven. His wife still sat with her knees apart, her feet on the steel fender and stared into the fire, motionless. Her skin was smooth and rosy in the firelight. Everything in the house was very clean and bright. The man sat silent, too, his head dropped. And thus they remained.

It was a question who would speak first. The woman leaned forward and poked the ends of the sticks in between the bars of the range. He lifted his head and looked at her.

"Others gone to bed, have they?" he asked.

But she remained closed in silence.

"'S a cold night, out," he said, as if to himself.

And he laid his large, yet well-shapen workman's hand on the top of the stove, that was polished black and smooth as velvet. She would not look at him, yet she glanced out of the corners of her eyes.

His eyes were fixed brightly on her, the pupils large and electric like those of a cat.

"I should have picked you out among thousands," he said.

"Though you're bigger than I'd have believed. Fine flesh you've made."

She was silent for some time. Then she turned in her chair upon him.

"What do you think of yourself," she said, "coming back on me like this after over fifteen years? You don't think I've not heard of you, neither, in Butte City[1] and elsewhere?"

He was watching her with his clear, translucent, unchallenged eyes.

"Yes," he said. "Chaps comes an' goes – I've heard tell of you from time to time."

She drew herself up.

"And what lies have you heard about *me*?" she demanded superbly.

"I dunno as I've heard any lies at all – ' cept as you was getting on very well, like."

His voice ran warily and detached. Her anger stirred again in her violently. But she subdued it, because of the danger there was in him, and more, perhaps, because of the beauty of his head and his level drawn brows, which she could not bear to forfeit.

"That's more than I can say of *you*," she said. "I've heard more harm than good about *you*."

"Ay, I dessay," he said, looking in the fire. It was a long time since he had seen the furze burning, he said to himself. There was a silence, during which she watched his face.

"Do you call yourself a *man*?" she said, more in contemptuous reproach than in anger. "Leave a woman as you've left me, you don't care to what! – and then to turn up in *this* fashion, without a word to say for yourself."

He stirred in his chair, planted his feet apart, and resting his arms on his knees, looked steadily into the fire, without answering. So near to her was his head, and the close black hair, she could scarcely refrain from starting away, as if it would bite her.

"Do you call that the action of a *man*?" she repeated.

"No," he said, reaching and poking the bits of wood into the fire with his fingers. "I didn't call it anything, as I know of. It's no good calling things by any names whatsoever, as I know of."

She watched him in his actions. There was a longer and

---

[1] a mining town in the American West

longer pause between each speech, though neither knew it.

"I *wonder* what you think of yourself!" she exclaimed with vexed emphasis "I *wonder* what sort of a fellow you take yourself to be!" She was really perplexed as well as angry.

"Well," he said, lifting his head to look at her, "I guess I'll answer for my own faults, if everybody else'll answer for theirs."

Her heart beat fiery hot as he lifted his face to her. She breathed heavily, averting her face, almost losing her self-control.

"And what do you take *me* to be?" she cried, in real helplessness.

His face was lifted watching her, watching her soft, averted face, and the softly heaving mass of her breasts.

"I take you," he said, with that laconic truthfulness which exercised such power over her, "to be the deuce of a fine woman – darn me if you're not as fine a built woman as I've seen, handsome with it as well. I shouldn't have expected you to put on such handsome flesh: 'struth I shouldn't."

Her heart beat fiery hot, as he watched her with those bright agate eyes, fixedly.

"Been very handsome to *you*, for fifteen years, my sakes!" she replied.

He made no answer to this, but sat with his bright, quick eyes upon her.

Then he rose. She started involuntarily. But he only said, in his laconic, measured way:

"It's warm in here now."

And he pulled off his overcoat, throwing it on the table. She sat as if slightly cowed, whilst he did so.

"Them ropes has given my arms something, by Ga-ard,"[1] he drawled, feeling his arms with his hands.

Still she sat in her chair before him, slightly cowed.

"You was sharp, wasn't you, to catch me like that, eh?" he smiled slowly. "By Ga-ard, you had me fixed proper, proper you had. Darn me, you fixed me up proper – proper, you did."

He leaned forwards in his chair towards her.

"I don't think no worse of you for it, no, darned if I do. Fine pluck in a woman's what I admire. That I do, indeed."

She only gazed into the fire.

"We fet from the start, we did. And, my word, you begin again quick the minute you see me, you did. Darn me, you was too

[1] God – spoken in an American accent

sharp for me. A darn fine woman, puts up a darn good fight. Darn me if I could find a woman in all the darn States as could get me down like that. Wonderful fine woman you be, truth to say, at this minute."

She only sat glowering into the fire.

"As grand a pluck as a man could wish to find in a woman, true as I'm here," he said, reaching forward his hand and tentatively touching her between her full, warm breasts, quietly.

She started, and seemed to shudder. But his hand insinuated itself between her breasts, as she continued to gaze in the fire.

"And don't you think I've come back here a-begging," he said. "I've more than *one* thousand pounds to my name, I have And a bit of a fight for a how-de-do pleases me, that it do. But that doesn't mean as you're going to deny as you're my Missis. . . ."

# A Handful of Thoughts

### Let Us be Men

For God's sake, let us be men
not monkeys minding machines
or sitting with our tails curled
while the machine amuses us, the radio or film or gramophone.

Monkeys with a bland grin on our faces.

### Self-pity

I never saw a wild thing
sorry for itself.
A small bird will drop frozen dead from a bough
without ever having felt sorry for itself.

### Wages

The wages of work is cash.
The wages of cash is want more cash.
The wages of want more cash is vicious competition.
The wages of vicious competition is – the world we live in.

The work-cash-want circle is the viciousest circle
that ever turned men into fiends.

Earning a wage is a prison occupation
and a wage-earner is a sort of gaol-bird.
Earning a salary is a prison overseer's job,
a gaoler instead of a gaol-bird.

Living on your income is strolling grandly outside the prison
in terror lest you have to go in. And since the work-prison covers
almost every scrap of the living earth, you stroll up and down
on a narrow beat, about the same as a prisoner taking his exercise.

This is called universal freedom.

## Revolution as Such!

Curiously enough, actual revolutions are made by robots,
living people never make revolutions,
they can't, life means too much to them.

## Robot Feelings

It is curious, too, that though the modern man in the street
is a robot, and incapable of love
he is capable of an endless, grinding, nihilistic hate:
that is the only strong feeling he is capable of;
and therein lies the danger of robot-democracy and all the men
   in the street,
they move in a great grind of hate, slowly but inevitably.

## Robot-Democracy

In a robot-democracy, nobody is willing to serve
even work is unwilling, the worker is unwilling, unwilling.

The great grind of unwillingness, the slow undergrind of hate
and democracy is ground into dust
then the mill-stones burst with the internal heat of their own
   friction.

## Property and No-property

The bourgeois asserts that he owns his property by divine right,
and the bolshevist asserts that by human right no man shall own
   property
and between the two blades of this pair of shears, property and
   no-property
we shall all be cut to bits.

# Death of a Gamekeeper

from the novel *The White Peacock*

*Annable is the generally unpopular gamekeeper on the estate of the local squire. The narrator of this episode, Cyril Beardsall, has managed to break through Annable's usually aggressive manner and has encountered underneath a disillusioned man. The two men have struck up a friendship and Annable has recently told Cyril about the sources of his disillusionment.*

Some four or five days after Annable had talked to me in the churchyard, I went out to find him again. It was Sunday morning. The larch-wood was afloat with clear, lyric green, and some primroses scattered whitely on the edge under the fringing boughs. It was a clear morning, as when the latent life of the world begins to vibrate afresh in the air. The smoke from the cottage rose blue against the trees, and thick yellow against the sky. The fire, it seemed, was only just lighted, and the wood-smoke poured out.

Sam appeared outside the house, and looked round. Then he climbed the water-trough for a better survey. Evidently unsatisfied, paying slight attention to me, he jumped down and went running across the hillside to the wood. "He is going for his father," I said to myself, and I left the path to follow him down hill across the waste meadow, crackling the blanched stems of last year's thistles as I went, and stumbling in rabbit holes. He reached the wall that ran along the quarry's edge, and was over it in a twinkling.

When I came to the place, I was somewhat nonplussed,[1] for, sheer from the stone fence, the quarryside dropped for some twenty or thirty feet, piled up with unmortared stones. I looked round – there was a plain dark thread down the hillside, which marked a path to this spot, and the wall was scored with the marks of heavy boots. Then I looked again down the quarryside, and I saw – how could I have failed to see? – stones projecting to make an uneven staircase, such as is often seen in the Derbyshire fences. I saw this ladder was well used, so I trusted myself to it, and scrambled down, clinging to the face of the quarry wall.

[1] puzzled

Once down, I felt pleased with myself for having discovered and used the unknown access, and I admired the care and ingenuity of the keeper, who had fitted and wedged the long stones into the uncertain pile.

It was warm in the quarry: there the sunshine seemed to thicken and sweeten; there the little mounds of overgrown waste were aglow with very early dog-violets; there the sparks were coming out on the bits of gorse, and among the stones the coltsfoot plumes were already silvery. Here was spring sitting just awake, unloosening her glittering hair, and opening her purple eyes.

I went across the quarry, down to where the brook ran murmuring a tale to the primroses and the budding trees. I was startled from my wandering among the fresh things by a faint clatter of stones.

"What's that young rascal doing?" I said to myself, setting forth to see. I came towards the other side of the quarry: on this, the moister side, the bushes grew up against the wall, which was higher than on the other side, though piled the same with old dry stones. As I drew near I could hear the scrape and rattle of stones, and the vigorous grunting of Sam as he laboured among them. He was hidden by a great bush of sallow catkins, all yellow, and murmuring with bees, warm with spice. When he came in view I laughed to see him lugging and grunting among the great pile of stones that had fallen in a mass from the quarryside; a pile of stones and earth and crushed vegetation. There was a great bare gap in the quarry wall. Somehow, the lad's labouring earnestness made me anxious, and I hurried up.

He heard me, and glancing round, his face red with exertion, eyes big with terror, he called, commanding me:

"Pull 'em off 'im – pull 'em off!"

Suddenly my heart beating in my throat nearly suffocated me. I saw the hand of the keeper lying among the stones. I set to tearing away the stones, and we worked for some time without a word. Then I seized the arm of the keeper and tried to drag him out. But I could not.

"Pull it off him!" whined the lad, working in a frenzy.

When we got him out I saw at once he was dead, and I sat down trembling with exertion. There was a great smashed wound on the side of the head. Sam put his face against his father's and snuffed round him like a dog, to feel the life in him. The child looked at me:

"He won't get up," he said, and his little voice was hoarse with fear and anxiety.

I shook my head. Then the boy began to whimper. He tried to close the lips which were drawn with pain and death, leaving the teeth bare; then his fingers hovered round the eyes, which were wide open, glazed, and I could see he was trembling to touch them into life.

"He's not asleep," he said, "because his eyes is open – look!"

I could not bear the child's questioning terror. I took him up to carry him away, but he struggled and fought to be free.

"Ma'e 'im get up – ma'e 'im get up," he cried in a frenzy, and I had to let the boy go.

He ran to the dead man, calling "Feyther![1] Feyther!" and pulling his shoulder; then he sat down, fascinated by the sight of the wound; he put out his finger to touch it, and shivered.

"Come away," said I.

"Is it that?" he asked, pointing to the wound. I covered the face with a big silk handkerchief.

"Now," said I, "he'll go to sleep if you don't touch him – so sit still while I go and fetch somebody. Will *you* run to the Hall?"

He shook his head. I knew he would not. So I told him again not to touch his father, but to let him lie still till I came back. He watched me go, but did not move from his seat on the stones beside the dead man, though I know he was full of terror at being left alone.

I ran to the Hall – I dared not go to the Kennels. In a short time I was back with the squire and three men. As I led the way, I saw the child lifting a corner of the handkerchief to peep and see if the eyes were closed in sleep. Then he heard us, and started violently. When we removed the covering, and he saw the face unchanged in its horror, he looked at me with a look I have never forgotten.

"A bad business – an awful business!" repeated the squire. "A bad business. I said to him from the first that the stones might come down when he was going up, and he said he had taken care to fix them. But you can't be sure, you can't be certain. And he'd be about half way up – ay – and the whole wall would come down on him. An awful business, it is really; a terrible piece of work!"

They decided at the inquest that the death came by mis-

[1] Father!

adventure. But there were vague rumours in the village that this was revenge which had overtaken the keeper.

They decided to bury him in our churchyard at Greymede under the beeches; the widow would have it so, and nothing might be denied her in her state.

It was a magnificent morning in early spring when I watched among the trees to see the procession come down the hillside. The upper air was woven with the music of the larks, and my whole world thrilled with the conception of summer. The young pale wind-flowers had arisen by the wood-gale, and under the hazels, when perchance the hot sun pushed his way, new little suns dawned, and blazed with real light. There was a certain thrill and quickening everywhere, as a woman must feel when she has conceived. A sallow[1] tree in a favoured spot looked like a pale gold cloud of summer dawn; nearer it had poised a golden, fairy busby on every twig, and was voiced with a hum of bees, like any sacred golden bush, uttering its gladness in the thrilling murmur of bees, and in warm scent. Birds called and flashed on every hand; they made off exultant with streaming strands of grass, or wisps of fleece, plunging into the dark spaces of the wood, and out again into the blue.

A lad moved across the field from the farm below with a dog trotting behind him – a dog, no, a fussy, black-legged lamb trotting along on its toes, with its tail swinging behind. They were going to the mothers on the common, who moved like little grey clouds among the dark gorse.

I cannot help forgetting, and sharing the spink's[2] triumph, when he flashes past with a fleece from a bramble bush. It will cover the bedded moss, it will weave among the soft red cow-hair beautifully. It is a prize, it is an ecstasy to have captured it at the right moment, and the nest is nearly ready.

Ah, but the thrush is scornful, ringing out his voice from the hedge! He sets his breast against the mud, and models it warm for the turquoise eggs – blue, blue, bluest of eggs, which cluster so close and round against the breast, which round up beneath the breast, nestling content. You should see the bright ecstasy in the eyes of a nesting thrush, because of the rounded caress of the eggs against her breast!

---

[1] a type of willow
[2] one of the finch family – probably the chaffinch

What a hurry the jenny wren makes – hoping I shall not see her dart into the low bush. I have a delight in watching them against their shy little wills. But they have all risen with a rush of wings, and are gone, the birds. The air is brushed with agitation. There is no lark in the sky, not one; the heaven is clear of wings or twinkling dot –.

Till the heralds come – till the heralds wave like shadows in the bright air, crying, lamenting, fretting forever. Rising and falling and circling round and round, the slow-waving peewits cry and complain, and lift their broad wings in sorrow. They stoop suddenly to the ground, the lapwings, then in another throb of anguish and protest, they swing up again, offering a glistening white breast to the sunlight, to deny it in black shadow, then a glisten of green, and all the time crying and crying in despair.

The pheasants are frightened into cover, they run and dart through the hedge. The cold cock must fly in his haste, spread himself on his streaming plumes, and sail into the wood's security.

There is a cry in answer to the peewits, echoing louder and stronger the lamentation of the lapwings, a wail which hushes the birds. The men come over the brow of the hill, slowly, with the old squire walking tall and straight in front, six bowed men bearing the coffin on their shoulders, treading heavily and cautiously, under the great weight of the glistening white coffin; six men following behind, ill at ease, waiting their turn for the burden. You can see the red handkerchiefs knotted round their throats, and their shirt-fronts blue and white between the open waistcoats. The coffin is of new unpolished wood, gleaming and glistening in the sunlight; the men who carry it remember all their lives after the smell of new, warm elm-wood.

Again a loud cry from the hill-top. The woman has followed thus far, the big, shapeless woman, and she cries with loud cries after the white coffin as it descends the hill, and the children that cling to her skirts weep aloud, and are not to be hushed by the other woman, who bends over them, but does not form one of the group. How the crying frightens the birds, and the rabbits; and the lambs away there run to their mothers. But the peewits are not frightened, they add their notes to the sorrow; they circle after the white, retreating coffin, they circle round the woman; it is they who forever "keen"[1] the sorrows of this world.

---

[1] wail. "Keening" is a ceremonial wailing for the dead

They are like priests in their robes, more black than white, more grief than hope, driving endlessly round and round, turning, lifting, falling and crying always in mournful desolation, repeating their last syllables like the broken accents of despair.

The bearers have at last sunk between the high banks, and turned out of sight. The big woman cannot see them, and yet she stands to look. She must go home, there is nothing left.

They have rested the coffin on the gate posts, and the bearers are wiping the sweat from their faces. They put their hands to their shoulders on the place where the weight has pressed.

The other six are placing the pads on their shoulders, when a girl comes up with a jug, and a blue pot. The squire drinks first, and fills for the rest. Meanwhile the girl stands back under the hedge, away from the coffin which smells of new elm-wood. In imagination she pictures the man shut up there in close darkness, while the sunlight flows all outside, and she catches her breast with terror. She must turn and rustle among the leaves of the violets for the flowers she does not see. Then, trembling, she comes to herself, and plucks a few flowers and breathes them hungrily into her soul, for comfort. The men put down the pots beside her, with thanks, and the squire gives the word. The bearers lift up the burden again, and the elm-boughs rattle along the hollow white wood, and the pitiful red clusters of elm-flowers sweep along it as if they whispered in sympathy – "We are so sorry, so sorry –"; always the compassionate buds in their fullness of life bend down to comfort the dark man shut up there. "Perhaps," the girl thinks, "he hears them, and goes softly to sleep." She shakes the tears out of her eyes on to the ground, and, taking up her pots, goes slowly down, over the brooks.

In a while, I too got up and went down to the mill, which lay red and peaceful, with the blue smoke rising as winsomely and carelessly as ever. On the other side of the valley I could see a pair of horses nod slowly across the fallow. A man's voice called to them now and again with a resonance that filled me with longing to follow my horses over the fallow, in the still, lonely valley, full of sunshine and eternal forgetfulness. The day had already forgotten. The water was blue and white and dark-burnished with shadows; two swans sailed across the reflected trees with perfect blithe grace. The gloom that had passed across was gone. I watched the swan with his ruffled wings swell onwards; I watched his slim consort go peeping into corners and under bushes; I saw him steer clear of the bushes, to keep full in view, turning his head to me imperiously, till I longed to pelt him with the empty husks of last year's flowers, knap-weed and scabious. I was too indolent, and I turned instead to the orchard.

There the daffodils were lifting their heads and throwing back their yellow curls. At the foot of each sloping, grey old tree stood a family of flowers, some bursten with golden fullness, some lifting their heads slightly, to show a modest, sweet countenance, others still hiding their faces, leaning forward pensively from the jaunty grey-green spears; I wished I had their language, to talk to them distinctly.

Overhead, the trees with lifted fingers shook out their hair to the sun, decking themselves with buds as white and cool as a water-nymph's breasts.

I began to be very glad. The colts-foot discs glowed and laughed in a merry company down the path; I stroked the velvet faces, and laughed also, and I smelled the scent of black-currant leaves, which is full of childish memories.

The house was quiet and complacent; it was peopled with ghosts again; but the ghosts had only come to enjoy the warm place once more, carrying sunshine in their arms and scattering it through the dusk of gloomy rooms.

# A Letter to David Chambers

*Ile de Port-Cros,*
*Var, France.*

14 *Novem.*, 1928

DEAR DAVID, –

I hardly recognized you as J. D. – and you must be a man now, instead of a thin little lad with very fair hair. Ugh, what a gap in time! it makes me feel scared.

Whatever I forget, I shall never forget the Haggs – I loved it so. I loved to come to you all, it really was a new life began in me there. The water-pippin by the door – those maidenblush roses that Flower would lean over and eat and trip floundering round. – And stewed figs for tea in winter, and in August green stewed apples. Do you still have them? Tell your mother I never forget, no matter where life carries us. – And does she still blush if somebody comes and finds her in a dirty white apron? Or doesn't she wear work-aprons any more? Oh, I'd love to be nineteen again, and coming up through the Warren and catching the first glimpse of the buildings. Then I'd sit on the sofa under the window, and we'd crowd round the little table to tea, in that tiny little kitchen I was so at home in.

*Son' tempi passati, cari miei! quanto cari, non saprete mai!* [1] – I could never tell you in English how much it all meant to me, how I still feel about it.

If there is anything I can ever do for you, do tell me. – Because whatever else I am, I am somewhere still the same Bert who rushed with such joy to the Haggs.

Ever,

D. H. LAWRENCE

---

[1] Those times have gone, my dear fellows! How dear you will never know!

# Points for Discussion and Suggestions for Writing

(Suggestions for your own writing are marked with an asterisk.)

### Rex

This is a true story of Lawrence's childhood. His mother thought that pets were unclean and her attitude towards them comes through in this story. The uncle in the tale was actually Mrs Lawrence's brother, Herbert Beardsall, who kept a pub, the Lord Belper, in the Sneinton area of Nottingham.

1 Discuss the ways in which Lawrence reveals the two sides of the dog's nature – that of a "fierce, canine little beast" and that of a creature with "a terrible, terrible necessity to love".

2 Do you agree with Lawrence when he says at the end of the story that "we should not have loved Rex so much, and he should not have loved us. . . . He should have stayed outside human limits, we should have stayed outside canine limits . . . "? What did the family do wrong in its training of Rex, do you think and how would *you* have trained him?

3 How in this account of Rex's behaviour does Lawrence reveal the sensitive understanding of animal nature which is often apparent elsewhere in his prose and poetry?

4 What do you learn about the Lawrence family from this story?

*5 Write an alternative ending to the story – continuing it in your own words from "And we began to feel that his heart was not so golden as we had imagined it" (page 8) and assuming that the uncle did not call for the dog and that the Lawrences kept it.

*6 Write your own story, true if possible, about the joys and sorrows of training a new pet in your home.

### A Quarrel

This episode is taken from Chapter 1, "The Early Married Life of the Morels", of Lawrence's autobiographical novel *Sons and Lovers*. It reflects the characters of Lawrence's parents Arthur and Lydia (the Morels of the story) and the violence of their quarrels, which took place often either in the presence or within the hearing of the children.

7　In what ways does Lawrence's account of the activities of the men on their outing and of the women at home reveal something of the traditional role of women in this mining community? How is this role also underlined by Mrs Morel's actions when she gets back in the house after having been put out into the garden?

8　Do you blame Morel for the outcome of this quarrel or do you think that Mrs Morel was partly responsible for the way it flared up?

9　How does Lawrence convey Mrs Morel's sense of confusion and bewilderment as she moves round the garden after Morel has put her out of the house?

*10　Write an account, real or imaginary, of a quarrel between two children which begins as a minor disagreement and eventually erupts into violence.

## The Return of Holroyd

This is the final episode, taken from Act 3, of the play *The Widowing of Mrs Holroyd*. It closely resembles the last pages of Lawrence's short story *Odour of Chrysanthemums*.

11　How does Lawrence build up the tension in this episode towards the point when Holroyd's body is carried into the house?

12　Discuss the roles of Rigley (Holroyd's working partner – or "butty") and the colliery manager in this episode. In what ways do their reactions to the tragedy differ?

13　What do you learn of the feelings of Mrs Holroyd and of her mother-in-law after the arrival of Holroyd's body? Can you see any signs of jealousy between them? In what ways do their attitudes to Holroyd's death reflect those of a wife and a mother-in-law respectively?

*14　Write an imaginary description of the scene at a pithead as relatives wait for news after a major mine disaster.

*15　Write a story, the climax of which is produced either by a quarrel between a wife and her mother-in-law or by a reconciliation between them.

## The Wedding

This is Chapter 5, "Wedding at the Marsh", from the novel *The Rainbow*. The church in the story is based on the one at

Cossall, a rural village a few miles from Eastwood. The cottage next door to the church, where Anna goes to live and where she spends her honeymoon, was in real life the home of Louie Burrows, a young woman to whom Lawrence was engaged for a short time.

16 What do you learn from this episode about Tom Brangwen's thoughts and feelings on Anna's wedding day?

17 Why do wedding days so often seem to inspire serious thoughts on the one hand and hilarity which often borders on the crude on the other?

18 How does Lawrence make all the characters so convincingly lifelike in his account of Anna's wedding? In what ways are the speeches typical of wedding celebrations of this kind?

19 Discuss the ways in which Lawrence, whilst admitting the fun of the wedding, emphasises its beauty, its dignity, and its underlying seriousness.

*20 Write a description of a wedding day as seen from the point of view of either the bride's father or the bridegroom's mother.

*21 Write a story, true if possible, entitled "The Family Gathering".

## A Sequence of Love Poems

*Last Words to Miriam*

"Miriam" was, in real life, Jessie Chambers. The tortured relationship between Jessie and Lawrence is explored at length in *Sons and Lovers*. This poem sums up Lawrence's view of the frustrations of the relationship, which foundered on the sexual inhibitions, at the time, of both Lawrence and "Miriam".

22 What appears to be Lawrence's interpretation of why the relationship with Miriam failed, as given in this poem?

23 What does the poem reveal of Lawrence's own nature? Look carefully at the images he uses of flowers, craftsmanship, fire, and crucifixion.

24 Write a carefully reasoned and *kind* farewell letter in which you explain why you wish to end a relationship.

*The Bride*

This was one of three poems Lawrence gave to Jessie Chambers to read when they were walking together on the day before his mother's funeral. In this poem he contemplates the appearance of his mother as she lies in death.

25 Discuss the significance of the title of the poem and its relation to the similes in the second and third verses.

26 How does Lawrence achieve a sense of beauty, dignity, and emotional restraint in this poem?

27 Lawrence watched his mother suffer a slow, painful death. For what reasons would he write this poem, do you think?

## Piano

Lawrence's great-grandfather on his mother's side wrote many hymns which were popular in non-conformist chapels. The Lawrences had a piano in their parlour at home and his mother would play hymns on it on Sunday evenings.

28 In what ways does this poem suggest that Lawrence is describing an experience which created memories disturbing in their intensity? What proof is there that it is *not* a sentimental piece of nostalgia?

29 Discuss the importance of word sounds in this poem and their contribution to the total effect of the poem.

*30 Write a story featuring a piece of music which has the power to remind the main character of something in his or her past which the character is anxious to forget.

## Bei Hennef

This poem is one of a number of poems about Frieda in the collection entitled "Look, We Have Come Through". These poems plot the difficult progress of Lawrence's emotional life as he sought to overcome the crisis caused by the loss of his mother and to find, in Frieda, a woman whom he could love and whose love would replace that of his mother. When Lawrence eloped to Europe with Frieda Weekley in 1912 he had to spend some days alone travelling in Germany before meeting Frieda at Munich for their "honeymoon". From Hennef on Rhine he wrote a postcard to Frieda whilst "sitting like a sad swain beside a nice, twittering little river, waiting for the twilight to drop, and my last train to come". He told her that "I know I only love you." The poem sums up his feelings as he sat "bei" (near) Hennef.

31 How does Lawrence use the twilight scene to reflect the uncertainties of the time since the death of his mother and the new certainty of his love for Frieda?

*32 Write a story in which the surroundings (town or country or both) reflect the sadness or the happiness of the tale.

## A Young Wife

This is another poem from "Look, We Have Come Through".

117

33 Discuss the significance of the sunshine, shadows, and darkness in this poem.

## A Letter to Mrs Hopkin

Sallie Hopkin was one of a number of middle-aged women with whom Lawrence became close friends in his youth at Eastwood. The friendship with Sallie extended also to her husband William, an enthusiastic socialist and local historian.

34 What does Lawrence reveal of himself at the time he wrote this letter? (Remember that before he met Frieda in 1912, he had had to face a succession of emotional crises in his relationship with, notably, Jessie Chambers, Louie Burrows and Helen Corke. His mother had died in December 1910 and during 1911 he had himself been seriously ill.)

## The Prussian Officer

This story was written when Lawrence and Frieda were in Bavaria in 1913. It grew from his observation and dislike of German militarism and from stories of army life told to him by Frieda – notably one about a German corporal who had once talked to her about the bullying that went on in the army.

35 How does the background of military manœuvres help to create and to maintain an atmosphere of tension in the story which is complementary to the tensions between the officer and the orderly?

36 Discuss the differences in character and temperament between the officer and his orderly. Do these differences contribute in any way to the events leading up to the final tragedies?

37 Discuss the reasons for the officer's cruel bullying of his orderly. Was the closed male society of army life in any way responsible for it?

38 How does Lawrence use details of the natural surroundings to indicate the progress of the orderly's fear and delirium after he has murdered the officer?

39 Discuss the effectiveness of the ending of the story.

*40 Write a story which describes a conflict resulting from the special tensions sometimes created within a single sex community.

*41 Write a story about bullying in which the bully holds a superior rank or position.

POINTS FOR DISCUSSION AND SUGGESTIONS FOR WRITING

## A Sequence of Nature Poems

*A Doe at Evening*
This is from the collection "Look, We Have Come Through".
It was written near Munich in 1912.
42 How does Lawrence create such a vivid impression of his
encounter with the doe?
43 Discuss the significance of the sight of the doe to Lawrence –
bearing in mind that he had recently eloped to Germany
from Nottingham with Frieda and that Frieda had left not
only her husband but also three children.
*44 Write a poem describing your impressions of a sudden
encounter with an animal or another creature during a
country walk.

*Bare Almond Trees*
This is one of the poems in the collection "Birds, Beasts and
Flowers". It was written when Lawrence was living at Taormina,
in Sicily, on the upper floor of an old farmhouse situated on
rising ground with olive, lemon, and almond trees all around,
and with extensive views out to sea and across to Sicily's great
volcano, Mount Etna.
45 Why is the scientific imagery of this poem so effective in
describing the winter appearance of the almond trees and in
conveying a mysterious sense of life in the trees despite their
bare, dead, wintry appearance?
46 How does Lawrence convey a powerful impression of the
atmosphere of the Sicilian landscape in winter?
*47 Write a description, in prose or verse, of a landscape known
to you, as you would see it in the starkness of winter.

*The Blue Jay*
This was written at a small ranch, Lobo, in New Mexico. In
a letter Lawrence described it as "a little ranch . . . about 150
acres, in the mountain foot-slopes, but two clearings – not much
water, though." The scenery was beautiful, the situation lonely.
"We have two little log houses and a tiny cabin."
48 How does Lawrence produce such vivid and precise impressions of the appearance and the characteristic behaviour of
the blue jay in this poem?
49 In what ways does the poem suggest Lawrence's happiness
in those surroundings at that moment?

*Mountain Lion*
This poem was also written during the time Lawrence was living at Lobo ranch.

50 Discuss the ways in which Lawrence creates a feeling of tension and menace as he describes his encounter with the two hunters.

51 How does Lawrence help his readers to gain clear mental pictures of the lion in death and of its appearance and movements in life?

52 Do you agree with the implications of Lawrence's statement: "Men! The only animal in the world to fear!"? Do you sympathise with his conclusions at the end of the poem as he looks out across the New Mexican landscape from the mountain lion's lair? Might you have reacted similarly in the surroundings described by Lawrence in the last three verses?

*53 Write a description of the hunting and killing of a wild animal which conveys clearly your strong disapproval of the hunters and your sympathy for the hunted.

## A Night at Mandas

This is taken from *Sea and Sardinia*, Lawrence's lively and entertaining account of a journey to the Mediterranean island of Sardinia which he made with Frieda in 1921 when they were living at Taormina, Sicily.

54 How does the preparedness of the Lawrences to accept the conditions of their overnight accommodation at Mandas and to enjoy contact with the local people add more interest and zest to Lawrence's account of the visit?

55 What makes Lawrence's descriptions of the landscapes around Mandas convey a strong sense of atmosphere?

56 Why do people read travel books? What are the ingredients of a good travel book? From the evidence of this episode what makes Lawrence a good travel writer?

*57 Write a description of a landscape which has particularly impressed you, giving not only details of its visual appearance but also some impression of its individual atmosphere.

*58 You are holidaying in a different part of this country, or in a foreign country. Write a letter home to a relative or friend, describing an evening spent in the company of the local people in the spot where you are staying.

## A Letter from Italy

Will Hopkin was an old Eastwood friend of Lawrence. Lawrence and Frieda rented the villa in Italy for the winter of 1913-14.

59  What impressions do you gain of Lawrence as a person from reading and studying this letter?

60  In what ways does the letter reveal Lawrence's gift for description and observation which he put to such effective use in his travel books?

## Samson and Delilah

The Cornish setting of this story is a reminder that Lawrence lived on the Land's End peninsula of Cornwall from February 1916 until October 1917, at a time when, because of the War, soldiers might be placed in temporary accommodation in private houses or pubs by the military authorities.

61  How does Lawrence make use of the atmospheric qualities of the Cornish scene and the Cornish nights to create interest and tension at the beginning of the story?

62  To what extent does this story owe its interest to the popular short story ingredient of the arrival of a mysterious stranger?

63  At what stage in the story do you think that the landlady recognises her husband?

64  Why do you think the landlady behaves in the way she does towards the stranger after he has announced himself to be her long-lost husband?

*65  Write a continuation of this story in which you resolve the question of whether the landlady takes her husband back or not.

*66  Write your own story about the effects on a family or on a small community of the arrival of a stranger in its midst.

## A Handful of Thoughts

The poems in this group have all been taken from collections of short poems written by Lawrence towards the end of his life. Lawrence called these poems "Pansies", and in his Introduction to the first collection he wrote:

"This little bunch of fragments is offered as a bunch of *pensées*, anglicé pansies; a handful of thoughts. Or, if you will have the other derivation of pansy, from *panser*, to dress or soothe a wound;

these are my tender administrations to the mental and emotional wounds we suffer from . . . "

67 What qualities in these short poems enable them to make their points so effectively?

68 Although the poems were written as Lawrence's response to industrial society as he saw it in the late 1920s, they are remarkably topical today. What dangers did Lawrence, in these poems, see existing in industrial society?

69 Is it the business of the professional writer to comment *directly* on what he considers to be unacceptable in the society in which he lives?

*70 Using simple sentence and verse structures similar to those employed by Lawrence, try writing a sequence of "protest" poems on social topics – in this country or abroad – about which you at present feel strongly.

## Death of a Gamekeeper

This is an episode taken from Lawrence's first novel, *The White Peacock*, set in the countryside not far from his home at Eastwood.

71 In what ways does this episode gain from being written in the first person?

72 How does Lawrence convey so strongly the sense of the "questioning terror" of the little boy Sam as he tries to help his father?

73 What early evidence does the description of the trees, flowers, birds, animals, and landscape in the vicinity of Greymede church and the mill give of Lawrence's sensitive powers of observation and of his informed interest in nature?

74 In what ways does Lawrence relate the natural surroundings to the events of the funeral?

*75 Write a story in which the human events described are reflected in the natural surroundings – landscape, weather and wild life – where these events take place.

## A Letter to David Chambers

David Chambers was one of the younger brothers of Jessie Chambers ("Miriam") at the Haggs farm, where Lawrence spent a great deal of time helping in his youth. The farm provided many of the settings in both *Sons and Lovers* and *The White Peacock*.

# Places and People in Lawrence's Life

The streets and buildings of the small mining town of Eastwood, ten miles west-north-west of Nottingham, are generally as uninteresting as those in any other town which has grown up around industry. The qualities which make Eastwood more interesting than many mining towns are its situation and its closeness to open countryside. The town occupies a breezy hill-top site overlooking the valley of the river Erewash. Lawrence, in his essay *Nottingham and the Mining Country*, wrote of an opportunity missed: Eastwood *"might* have been like the lovely hill-towns of Italy, shapely and fascinating". Instead, he pointed out in the same essay, the local colliery owners built "sordid and hideous houses" and "dared to perpetrate the ugliness of my native village". Eastwood, however, still retains some benefits of situation. Little more than a mile to the north east, beyond the grounds of Lamb Close, home of the family whose ancestors developed the local coal mine, lies the lonely expanse of Moor Green reservoir, and beyond that is an area of attractive hilly country. The countryside there has changed little since D.H. Lawrence was born in nearby Eastwood on 11 September 1885, the fourth of five children, of whom four were sons.

His parents were an ill-matched pair. Arthur Lawrence, the father, was a miner, a lively man, with ordinary tastes. He liked the company of his mates, was a good dancer, and enjoyed a drink. Lydia Lawrence, the mother, had been, for a short time before her marriage, a school-teacher. She came from a family of chapel-goers, enjoyed polite company and intellectual talk, and was very house-proud. The differences between father and mother quickly became a recipe for quarrels, sometimes violent, as Lydia Lawrence's distaste for her husband's occupation, his enjoyments, his friends, and his drinking increased. As relations worsened, so Mrs Lawrence grew closer to her children, encouraged her sons to take her side against their father, and became passionately determined that her sons would not become coal-miners.

From the start Lawrence – Bert to his family and friends – was a thin, frail, delicate child who was unable to take part in the usual active pursuits of small boys. Always sensitive, he was not happy at his first school, where the boys jeered at him for not playing games and for preferring the company of the girls. He was a gentle child, yet he was also eager, friendly and determined. He was well coached at the local junior school for a scholarship to Nottingham High School and he won one in 1898. His mother saved hard in order to keep him there until 1901, when he left and took up his first job as a junior clerk with a firm manufacturing surgical appliances in Nottingham. However, in October 1901 the family was shattered by the death of Bert's brother Ernest in London. Up to that time Mrs Lawrence's greatest hopes had rested in Ernest, who had been her favourite son. Now she had new problems to face, for Bert, the strain of several years of travelling to and from Nottingham in all weathers proving too much for his delicate constitution, became seriously ill with pneumonia. Bert recovered, but it had been touch and go, and during the early months of 1902 it became clear that his mother had adopted Bert as her favourite and was going to pin all her hopes both on his survival and on his future success.

In the autumn of 1902 he became a pupil-teacher (a position then rather like that of an apprentice) at a local school, and the following year he started training at the Pupil-Teacher Centre at the nearby town of Ilkeston. Two years later he took on a year's work as an uncertificated teacher at Eastwood in order to save up the advance fees for admission to university. From 1906 to 1908 he studied for his Teaching Certificate at University College, Nottingham, and received his certificate in June, 1908. Meanwhile, many incidents of greater significance had been occurring outside the sphere of his professional studies.

On a summer day in 1901 Mrs Lawrence took Bert with her to visit a Mrs Chambers, whom she had met at the local chapel. The Chambers family lived at Haggs Farm in the lonely countryside beyond Moor Green reservoir. Bert was entranced by the walk there through the woods and fields, and he was equally impressed by the farm and by the Chambers family. During 1902, after his illness, he took to visiting the farm alone, and he quickly became regarded as one of the family. He assisted Mrs Chambers in the house, cleaning the hearth and peeling vegetables, and helped Mr Chambers and his sons out in the fields. He became close friends with two of the Chambers children, Jessie and Alan. Jessie later recalled her father's saying, "Work goes like fun when Bert's here", and Mrs Chambers once said, "I should like to be next to Bert in heaven."

Jessie Chambers was Bert's first love. She was shy, sensitive, and intelligent and Bert was first attracted to her by her seriousness and her interest in books and study. They read and studied together a wide range of literature, poetry, French and even philosophy. Alan often joined their discussions. Bert's mother soon became bitterly jealous of Jessie. She was particularly resentful of the way in which Bert turned to Jessie for intellectual companionship. His relationship with Jessie was one of the most intense and significant in his whole life and it undoubtedly released the artist in Lawrence. This his mother could not bear and in her fight to overcome Jessie's influence she made unscrupulous use of her son's intense love for her, inflicting long-lasting emotional problems on him in the process.

Lawrence's friendship with Jessie did not by any means exclude other friendships. In the early 1900s Lawrence, Jessie, and Alan were part of a larger group of friends, all of whom had lively, enquiring minds – a group significantly calling itself "the Pagans". "The Pagans" included an attractive girl, Louisa ("Louie") Burrows, to whom Lawrence later became engaged for a short time. He also made another important friend at this time, William Hopkin, an older man who was a committed socialist and who later became a source of important contacts. All these friends helped to widen Lawrence's intellectual horizons, but it was Jessie Chambers who was the driving force in encouraging him to write his first poems and, in 1906, to begin writing his first novel, *The White Peacock*.

In 1908 Lawrence left Eastwood to take up his first teaching post at Davidson Road Boys' School, Croydon, where he worked hard, enthusiastically and, sometimes, despairingly for three years. People who knew him at school later remembered that he got on well with his colleagues, was always friendly, and was lively and enthusiastic in discussions. He was not always tolerant of authority, however. Away from Jessie, Lawrence became close friends with a young woman teacher and writer, Helen Corke. Helen was something of a substitute for Jessie whilst Lawrence was in Croydon and she too inspired his writing. Meanwhile, Jessie sent off some of his poems to a magazine, *The English Review*. When they were published it was Jessie who accompanied Lawrence to his first literary luncheon in London – his first contact with the London literary world.

At home during this period Lawrence intensified his romantic relationship with his long-standing "Pagan" friend, Louie Burrows. On his visits to Eastwood he met many eminent social reformers at the home of William Hopkin and also became friends with an unconventional blonde, Mrs Alice Dax, a suffragette and women's rights campaigner.

The most traumatic incident in Lawrence's life occurred in 1910. In August of that year cancer was diagnosed in his mother. She died, after much suffering witnessed by her anguished son, in December. Lawrence returned to Croydon, but in November 1911 he again became seriously ill with pneumonia. In January 1912 he went to Bournemouth to convalesce and by February he was back in Eastwood. He did not return to teaching in Croydon, but stayed with his sister Ada and continued with the writing of his latest novel, *Sons and Lovers*.

In April 1912 a visit to the home of Professor Ernest Weekley, who had taught him French at University College Nottingham, completely and dramatically changed his life. There he met Mrs Weekley for the first time. She was tall, blonde, and beautiful. Daughter of a German aristocrat, Friedrich von Richthofen, she was bored with her marriage to an academic fifteen years her senior. When she talked alone with Lawrence for half an hour before lunch she was briefly resentful of Lawrence's direct manner, but she quickly became aware that he rekindled her zest for life which marriage had extinguished. Further meetings soon followed and Frieda and Lawrence fell in love. Less than a month after their first encounter Frieda left her husband and three children and travelled to Germany with Lawrence. After visiting Metz, where her family lived, they spent a week's "honeymoon" in Bavaria before walking across the Alps into Italy. Once in Italy they settled for seven months at Gargnano, near Lake Garda.

They returned to London in the summer of 1913. In London they made some important contacts with figures in London literary circles. Two of these figures became close friends for several years – the magazine editor John Middleton Murry and the writer Katherine Mansfield. By the winter Lawrence and Frieda were once again in Italy. They returned to London when Frieda's divorce from Professor Weekley became final, and they married on 13 July 1914. Less than a month later Britain was at war with Germany.

There is no doubt that Lawrence found in Frieda a woman

whose love and whose strength of character were capable of filling the vacuum left inside him by the death of his mother. From the start, even during their first journey through Europe in 1912, there were struggles and quarrels, but these were more than counterbalanced by the great happiness they found in each other. The extent of their true happiness was sometimes underestimated by friends who witnessed their frequent quarrels. These were dramatic and violent affairs, often involving the hurling of crockery at each other. Yet they seemed to act as useful outlets for the release of tensions within their individual personalities, and it must be emphasised that their relationship was deep, tender, and lasting, and that the unique strength of Frieda's personality was the most stabilising influence in Lawrence's adult life.

During the war years from 1914 to 1918 the Lawrences, unable to leave England, led a restless life. They rented a damp cottage in Buckinghamshire, where Lawrence was frequently ill, spent six months in a cottage in Sussex, and then, after a spell in London, moved to Cornwall. In 1915 Lawrence was embittered by the seizing of copies of *The Rainbow* by the police and by the subsequent public declaration that it was an obscene book.

Lawrence liked Cornwall at first. In 1916 he and Frieda managed to rent a cottage near Zennor. It was situated high up on the hills of the Land's End peninsula and looked across to the Atlantic. Lawrence made friends with a young Cornish farmer and enjoyed helping on the farm just as he had enjoyed helping at Haggs farm in his youth. The Cornish idyll soured. In 1917 the unfounded suspicions of local people that the Lawrences were communicating with German submarines off the Cornish coast led to their cottage being ransacked by the army and the police and to a military request that they should leave Cornwall within three days. They returned to London in October 1917. More moves followed. After staying with the writer Richard Aldington in London they moved to a cottage owned by friends in Berkshire, then to a cottage in the Derbyshire hills, and finally back to Berkshire, where they were living when the war ended in 1918.

During the war years Lawrence had been obsessed with the idea of getting out of England for good and establishing an artists' colony, to be called Rananim, with a group of specially invited intellectual friends. One plan was to go off to the

United States to establish Rananim at the Florida home of English composer Frederick Delius, but Delius was not enthusiastic. Another plan was to establish Rananim in a remote part of the Andes in South America. One of Lawrence's friends at this time was the eccentric aristocratic patron of fashionable intellectuals Lady Ottoline Morrell. For a time Lawrence had ideas of establishing a sort of English Rananim at Lady Ottoline's country home at Garsington, near Oxford, but this came to nothing, as did his attempt, in Cornwall, to persuade John Middleton Murry to establish a blood-brotherhood with him.

It was hardly surprising that with his working-class background Lawrence often actively disliked the fashionable intellectuals with whom he became acquainted. They tended to increase his aggressiveness in upholding his ideals, and the arguments which ensued led to spitefulness and petulance on both sides. Lawrence took delight in putting a number of these intellectuals into his novels, where they appeared, wittily and occasionally wickedly, as major and minor characters, often put in their place by the character who represented Lawrence himself! In *Women in Love* Gudrun Brangwen bears close resemblances to Katherine Mansfield, Gerald Crich draws some of his characteristics from John Middleton Murry, Hermione Roddice is a waspishly satirical portrait of Lady Ottoline Morrell, Halliday resembles the musician Philip Heseltine (who considered legal action when he recognised himself), and Sir Joshua Mattheson ("a learned, dry Baronet of fifty, who was always making witticisms and laughing at them heartily in a harsh horse-laugh") is a delicious send-up of the eminent philosopher Bertrand Russell. It is only fair to add that the character of Birkin, a self-portrait of Lawrence, reveals Lawrence's honest capacity to see his own faults too.

In the autumn of 1919 the Lawrences were able to obtain passports and in October they made their final break with England. After wintering in Italy they settled in March 1920 at Taormina, on the island of Sicily, where they remained happily for two years. For Lawrence it was a time of intensive writing – of many of the "Birds, Beasts and Flowers" collection of poems (including the famous "Snake") and of the novels *The Lost Girl* and *Aaron's Rod*. In January of 1921 Lawrence and Frieda sailed to Sardinia and toured the island, a journey to be recorded by Lawrence in his fine travel book *Sea and Sardinia*.

Eventually Lawrence wanted to move on again. By chance, at a time when they were thinking of the possibilities of moving to America – Mexico, New Mexico and The Rockies were considered – they received an offer of the use of a traditional adobe house ("adobe" is an unburnt brick dried in the sun) on the estate of a rich American woman, Mabel Dodge Sterne, at Taos, New Mexico. Like Lady Ottoline Morrell, Mabel Dodge Sterne cultivated trendy literary and artistic people. She had been impressed by Lawrence's *Sea and Sardinia*: perhaps he could write about Taos. Lawrence was hesitant. He stalled for a time by sailing, with Frieda, to Ceylon in February 1922, and then to Australia. The couple visited Western Australia and Sydney, and then rented a house on the coast forty miles from Sydney. Eventually they got to Taos, via New Zealand, Tahiti, and San Francisco.

They arrived at Taos on 22 September 1922. Lawrence quickly discovered that he disliked the overbearing Mabel Dodge Sterne. He also disliked the American literary characters in her circle and – in fact – the whole American way of life. Nevertheless, he loved the New Mexican landscapes intensely and was fascinated by the native people, their customs, and their religion. Lawrence read a great deal about Mexico and the Aztec religion and this reading together with his experiences out there provided the inspiration for his adventurous, difficult novel *The Plumed Serpent*.

Between 1923 and 1925 the Lawrences lived in both New Mexico and Mexico. Lawrence particularly enjoyed the time spent living at a remote ranch on Lobo Mountain in New Mexico, where the life was hard but the climate was good for his health. Mexico, however, was much less healthy, and as a result of their spending the winter of 1924–25 in Mexico and of his struggling there to finish *The Plumed Serpent* Lawrence became extremely ill. He was now plainly suffering from tuberculosis and doctors in Mexico City told Frieda they expected him to live only a year at the most. Against all odds Lawrence regained his strength once back at Lobo Ranch, and for a time he began to enjoy life again amidst the beautiful scenery.

He was, unfortunately, back in the United States on a temporary visa, and he knew that because of his ill-health it would not be renewed. In September 1925 he and Frieda left the ranch, trekking to England and then across Europe to Italy, where eventually they rented a villa a few miles from Florence. Here, despite declining health, he was again happy. He wrote a large number of poems (many of them short, cryptic comments on life and now collected under the title of "Pansies"), his last novel, *Lady Chatterley's Lover*, a fine short story, "The Man Who Died", and, after a visit with a friend to the Etruscan ruins and tombs near Rome, his last, serene travel book, *Etruscan Places*.

Time was now beginning to run out for him. In the summer of 1927 a combination of heat and overwork brought on a serious lung haemorrhage, and he decided to leave Italy. For a time, in 1928, the Lawrences lived in the Alps, where he not only wrote a number of journalistic essays but also produced a number of paintings. In 1930 an English tuberculosis specialist visited Lawrence in southern France, where the Lawrences were then living. He immediately recommended that Lawrence should enter a sanatorium at Vence, and Lawrence did so in February 1930. His condition deteriorated and, knowing he was dying, he left the sanatorium on 1st March. He was moved to a villa in Vence where, with Frieda at his bedside, he died on the evening of 2nd March.

The Lawrence family. "Bert" is standing between his mother and father.

The Chambers family at Haggs Farm, c. 1906 – the "Leivers" family and the "Willey Farm" of *Sons and Lovers*.

The Breach, Eastwood. Lawrence lived there between the ages of two and seven, in an end house.

Brinsley Colliery, Eastwood, around 1920. Lawrence's father worked there.

The kitchen of a miner's house.

Cossall church ("Cossethay"), scene of Anna Brangwen's wedding in *The Rainbow*.

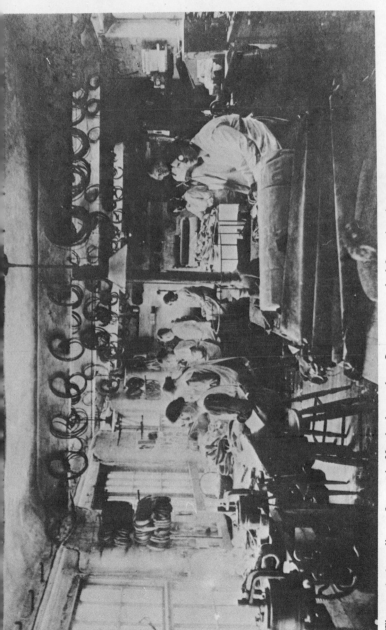

The surgical appliance factory in Nottingham where Lawrence worked for a time in 1901.

Louie Burrows, whose looks Lawrence gave to Clara Dawes in *Sons and Lovers* and to Ursula Brangwen in *The Rainbow*. Lawrence was engaged to her for a short time.

Jessie Chambers of Haggs Farm, Lawrence's first love. She was Miriam in *Sons and Lovers*.

Frieda, around 1912, the year she eloped with Lawrence.

Helen Corke, Lawrence's friend while he was teaching at Croydon.

Lawrence's mother, Mrs Lydia Lawrence, during her last illness.

Lawrence under an Italian olive tree.

# What to Read Next

The recommendations which follow are intended as a guide to readers who have enjoyed the present selection, who wish to read more of Lawrence's work, and who wish at this stage to avoid the more difficult writings.

### The Novels

The best one to start with is undoubtedly *Sons and Lovers*. A good autobiographical novel can bring its readers far closer to its subject than any biography. In *Sons and Lovers* we meet Lawrence, as "Paul Morel", in his formative years. We join his family in the fearful moments of his parents' quarrels, in the rarer happy times when his father is a warm member of the family circle, in the tragedy of a son's death. We accompany the sensitive young Lawrence as he goes to the interview for his first job, and we observe his embarrassments during his first days at work as a junior clerk in Nottingham.

Later in the novel the focus narrows and the novel's title becomes more significant as Lawrence describes, through Paul and Miriam, the progress of his first vital friendship with a girl, Jessie Chambers, and his mother's bitter opposition to the friendship. Few novels have explored so convincingly the pleasures, the pains, the intensity, the frustrations and the hesitancies of a first love affair and its effects on the relationship between an over-possessive but deeply loving and caring mother and a bewildered loving son and lover. Perhaps no other novelist has faced up so courageously to the task of describing the slow, lingering and painful death of a character who was in life his own mother. The closing chapters of the novel underline the poignancy of his mother's death and the devastating effect of it on Lawrence himself.

*The White Peacock*, Lawrence's first novel, is one of his easiest novels to read. It is written in the first person and this adds to the warm intimacy of the writing which is such an enjoyable feature of this novel. The narrator is Cyril Beardsall, a character clearly based on that of Lawrence himself, and his dialogues with his other young friends in the story have an engaging intellectual zest which probably mirrors that of Lawrence in his youth.

The most attractive quality in *The White Peacock* is Lawrence's writing about nature and the countryside. From the day his mother first took him to visit the Chambers family at the Haggs farm in his sixteenth year Lawrence loved the unspoilt countryside around the farm, and most of his first novel is set in that countryside. Reading it you may sometimes gain the impression that you are being walked through it in Lawrence's enthusiastically observant company. You pause to watch "the shadowy fish slide through the gloom of the mill pond", to examine "here and there among the marshy places ragged nests of water-fowl, now deserted", or to listen as "a corn-crake talked to me across the valley, talked and talked endlessly, asking and answering in hoarse tones from the sleeping, mist-hidden meadows". It is a novel which contains many moments of beauty and some moments of sadness, but which also possesses a feeling of freedom – that of a young writer revelling in his craft and of a young man as yet unaffected by the shadows of the world.

*The Lost Girl* is also a relatively easy novel to read. The Lost Girl is the heroine of the story, Alvina Houghton, and her experiences reflect those of many young men and women who have felt trapped by conventional family and local environments. Alvina is saddled with a father whose business enterprises – his draper's shop, his "Pleasure Palace" for films and live entertainment, and his private coal mine – were all doomed to failure. Marriage seems the only way out of a tedious spinsterhood in a dowdy industrial town, yet Alvina dislikes the idea of a conventional marriage to a conventional professional man. After meeting a young Italian, Ciccio, who is performing in a tatty theatrical company playing at the "Pleasure Palace", Alvina goes off with the company for a time, attracted both by Ciccio and by the off-beat travelling life. Eventually she marries Ciccio and returns to Italy with him, only to find that out there she is even more a "lost girl ... cut off from everything she belonged to".

In this novel you will find that, in contrast to *Sons and Lovers* and *The White Peacock*, Lawrence writes in a rather staccato, mocking style, the brusque sentences of which go well with the entertaining and breezily depressing account of Houghton's various business failures. The mildly comic and sometimes ridiculous happenings at the cinema and amongst the theatricals are a welcome contrast to the realistic dreariness of the world outside, whilst the alien quality of life for Alvina when she joins Ciccio's family in Italy is effectively presented.

*The Rainbow* should be your eventual goal. This noble, often difficult, novel represents Lawrence's writing at its most sensitive and inspired. It is perhaps more profound, though less difficult to enjoy and appreciate, than its sequel, *Women in Love*. This is partly because it is constructed to a familiar pattern, that of the family chronicle novel covering the lives of representatives of three generations of a long established family of farming stock, the Brangwens. Lawrence's narrative of events in those lives is direct and the use of dialogue is economical and realistic. The supporting descriptions of surroundings contain some of Lawrence's most evocative writing. The analysis of his characters' search for physical and spiritual fulfilment in their relationships, a process symbolised by the rainbow arch linking the earthly and the heavenly – the body and the spirit – is additional to the narrative. As a result you will find that the dialogue is never weighed down with lengthy intellectual discussions between the characters, as is sometimes the case in the later novels.

Read it then, in the first place, as the Brangwen family's story, rich in incident and full of pathos. At the beginning, for instance, observe Tom Brangwen, a young farmer, facing not only the initial problems of courting the attractive widow of a Polish doctor but also the greater problem of winning the love and acceptance of his step-daughter Anna after his marriage. The story of how he wins over Anna so that she "looked from one to the other, and she saw them established as her safety, and and she was free" is one of the most moving in the whole of Lawrence's writing.

Of the remaining novels, *Women in Love* is undoubtedly the finest, but it is better to come to it later rather than sooner. Unlike *The Rainbow*, it requires from its reader a special preparedness to follow the frequently complex arguments in the dialogues between its characters. To be enjoyed to the full, it also requires some knowledge of the originals of some of the key characters, knowledge which will enable you to see how devastatingly true to their originals these characters are! The same advice goes for *Aaron's Rod* which, although not in the same class as *Women in Love*, contains some almost cruelly perceptive studies of some of Lawrence's acquaintances.

*Kangaroo* and *The Plumed Serpent* are essentially novels of ideas, containing some of Lawrence's most difficult and taxing writing. You may, however, enjoy reading Chapter 12, "The Nightmare", in *Kangaroo*. This can be read virtually as a tale in itself – a thinly disguised account of Lawrence's unhappy experiences in Cornwall during the First World War. In the story Lawrence appears as Richard Somers.

"I always labour at the same thing, to make the sex relation valid and precious instead of shameful. And this novel is the furthest I've gone." So Lawrence wrote of *Lady Chatterley's Lover*. If you decide to read this novel, which is tender in its treatment of sex but angry in its assessment of modern money-grubbing society and of life in industrial communities, consider the following thoughts about the importance of the novel as a reflection of life:

> "Therefore, the novel, properly handled, can reveal the most secret places of life; for it is in the *passional* secret places of life, above all, that the tide of sensitive awareness needs to ebb and flow, cleansing and freshening."

These words are Lawrence's challenge to his readers' integrity, thrown down in a passage from the novel it upheld, *Lady Chatterley's Lover*.

## The Short Stories

Lawrence wrote a large number of short stories. Many of these form an ideal introduction to the worlds of the novels as well as being attractive to read. Here are a few recommendations:

*The Miner at Home:* A sketch rather than an extended story describing a wife's opposition to her miner husband's decision to obey a strike call from the union and the heated argument which results.

*Her Turn:* Another story with a strike background, but with an element of grim comedy in its account of a miner's wife who finally persuades her husband to hand over some of his strike pay by spending what spare cash she has left on things for the house rather than on food for him!

*Strike Pay:* The best of Lawrence's strike stories. A miner who spends his strike pay on a trip to Nottingham has to face a formidable mother-in-law when he returns home.

*Odour of Chrysanthemums:* Probably Lawrence's finest short story. A miner's wife waits angrily for her husband to come home, thinking he has spent the evening getting drunk, but he has been killed at the pit and his homecoming is a silent one.

*The Christening:* A harshly effective story describing the tensions of the day when a minister visits a miner's home to christen the baby born to the miner's unmarried daughter.

*Tickets, Please:* John Thomas, a tram inspector, is notorious for his flirtations with the wartime tram conductresses. They decide to teach him a lesson, but in the horseplay of their revenge John Thomas is not the only one whose feelings are hurt.

*Adolf:* A true story of a rabbit brought home for the children by Lawrence's father.

*The Horse-Dealer's Daughter:* The local doctor rescues the daughter from the pond in which she has tried to drown herself. He finds himself suddenly in love with her and yet shocked by the intrusion of love into what began as a doctor-patient situation. A powerful and moving story.

*Love Among The Haystacks:* A misleadingly coy title for one of Lawrence's most satisfying short stories. Two brothers, "both fiercely shy of women", are harvesting in a family-owned field four miles from the home farm. During the harvesting both fall in love for the first time as a result of two unusual encounters, the younger brother's with a young German governess from the nearby vicarage, the elder brother's with the neglected but sensitive and attractive wife of a tramp whom she has abandoned.

*The Rocking Horse Winner:* A disturbing story of the uncanny. Paul, young son in a middle class family obsessed by the need for more and more money to keep up social appearances, finds he can predict race winners whilst riding his rocking horse. He is encouraged, but the mental strain brings on a brain fever which kills him. His mother is left "eight-odd thousand to the good, and a poor devil of a son to the bad".

*Monkey Nuts:* Towards the end of the First World War a shy young soldier stationed in the English countryside has to defend himself against a more deadly foe than the Germans – a pretty land-girl who is determined to conquer him.

*Wintry Peacock:* Just before her soldier husband returns home from Belgium his wife asks an acquaintance to translate a letter sent to him by a girl out there. When the acquaintance scans the letter he finds it is a love-letter and, more, it tells of the birth of her baby – the father of whom is the soldier. The acquaintance discreetly provides a less incriminating translation. . . .

## The Travel Writings

Of Lawrence's travel writings, the book which is the most entertaining is *Sea and Sardinia*. It is a lively, beautifully observed, and often comic account of the Lawrences' visit to Sardinia in 1921. You will find it one of his sunniest books, reflecting a welcome time of contentment in his life.

The other travel writings are often more difficult to read because they often include philosophical meditations of varying degrees of complexity. If you are interested in ancient history and respond to the atmosphere of ruins and tombs you may enjoy reading the whole of Lawrence's superb final travel book, the short *Etruscan Places*, a record of his visit to the tombs and ruins of the ancient Etruscan civilisation close to Rome.

## The Plays

You should certainly read the whole of *The Widowing of Mrs Holroyd* and you would probably also enjoy *The Daughter-in-Law*. Both plays, set in the mining communities Lawrence knew so well, illustrate Lawrence's ability to create powerful theatre out of the tensions in relationships within these communities. The plays are available in a Heinemann Educational edition which contains a helpful introduction to them by Michael Marland.

## The Essays

Many of these are difficult reading, but try "Nottingham and the Mining Country", a fascinating account of Lawrence's home area as well as being an eloquent and still topical plea for imaginative town planning.

## The Poems

Some of Lawrence's poetry requires a great deal of study to understand fully, but he wrote a great deal of poetry which can be enjoyed and understood by the general reader. Here are a few recommendations. They can all be found in *The Complete Poems of D. H. Lawrence Vol. 1* edited by V. De Sola Pinto and

Warren Roberts (Heinemann).

1 from "Rhyming Poems" – poems from the years before he met Frieda:

> *Dog-Tired, Discord In Childhood, Love On The Farm, Monologue Of A Mother, End Of Another Home Holiday, A Winter's Tale, Return, Lilies In The Fire, Reminder, Sorrow, The Inheritance, Brooding Grief, Excursion Train, Kisses In The Train, Turned Down, Snap-Dragon.*

2 from "Unrhyming Poems" – "Look, We Have Come Through":

Lawrence, in a Foreword, described these poems as "The intrinsic experience of a man during the crisis of manhood, when he marries and comes into himself."

> *Elegy, The Sea, First Morning, On The Balcony, River Roses, History, Song Of A Man Who Has Come Through.*

3 from "Birds, Beasts and Flowers":

> *The Mosquito, Bat, Snake, Baby Tortoise, Humming-Bird, Eagle, Kangaroo.*

4 from "Pansies":

There are too many of these very short, frequently controversial, often cynical, always stimulating poems to list. If you have enjoyed "A Handful of Thoughts" in this selection, explore these!

# Reading about D.H. Lawrence

F.B. Pinion: *A D.H. Lawrence Companion*, Macmillan 1978.
The latest in Pinion's excellent "Companion" books (previous books cover Thomas Hardy, Jane Austen and The Brontes), full of information about Lawrence and about the characters and places in his writings. An ideal acquisition for the school library.

Harry T. Moore: *The Intelligent Heart. The Story of D.H. Lawrence*, Heinemann 1955.
A detailed yet highly readable study of Lawrence's life and work, invaluable for any extended study of Lawrence.

Richard Aldington: *Portrait of a Genius But . . .* , Heinemann 1951.
A more subjective biography by a writer who knew Lawrence well, and a book which, in dwelling on Lawrence's quarrels with friends and acquaintances, also reveals something of the friends themselves.

"E.T.": *D.H. Lawrence: A Personal Record*, Jonathan Cape.
"E.T." is Jessie Chambers, the "Miriam" of *Sons and Lovers*. A valuable opportunity to look at the relationship between Lawrence and Jessie Chambers as she saw it.

Frieda Lawrence: *Not I But The Wind*, Heinemann.
An authentic view of life with Lawrence.

Two useful short studies of Lawrence are:

Kenneth Young: *D.H. Lawrence*, Longman.
A brief, informative survey in the "Writers and their Work" series.

Chris Buckton: *D.H. Lawrence*, Longman Group Resources Unit 1978.
A most useful student introduction to the life and major works of Lawrence as they relate to the times in which he lived, supported by imaginatively selected drawings and maps. This is one of the "Writers In Their Time" series.

**Longman Imprint Books**
*General Editor:* Michael Marland

Titles in the series
**There is a Happy Land** Keith Waterhouse
**Nine African Stories** Doris Lessing
**The Experience of Colour** *edited by* Michael Marland
*****The Human Element and other stories** Stan Barstow
*****The Leaping Lad and other stories** Sid Chaplin
**Z Cars** Four television scripts
**Steptoe and Son** Four television scripts
**Conflicting Generations** Five television scripts
*****A Sillitoe Selection** *edited by* Michael Marland
***** Late Night on Watling Street and other stories** Bill Naughton
**Black Boy** Richard Wright
**The Millstone** Margaret Drabble
**Fair Stood the Wind for France** H.E. Bates
**A Way of Life and other stories** Dan Jacobson
**Scene Scripts** Seven television plays
**The Experience of Work** *edited by* Michael Marland
**Breaking Away** *edited by* Marilyn Davies *and* Michael Marland
**The Kraken Wakes** John Wyndham
**A Hemingway Selection** *edited by* Dennis Pepper
**Friends and Families** *edited by* Eileen *and* Michael Marland
**Ten Western Stories** *edited by* C.E.J. Smith
**The Good Corn and other stories** H.E. Bates
**The Experience of Sport** *edited by* John L. Foster
*****Loves, Hopes, and Fears** *edited by* Michael Marland
**The African Queen** C.S. Forester
*****A Casual Acquaintance and other stories** Stan Barstow
**Eight American Stories** *edited by* D.L. James
**Cider with Rosie** Laurie Lee
**The L-Shaped Room** Lynne Reid Banks
**Softly, Softly** Five television scripts by Elwyn Jones
**The Pressures of Life** Four television plays
**The Experience of Prison** *edited by* David Ball
**Saturday Night and Sunday Morning** Alan Sillitoe
*****A John Wain Selection** John Wain
**Jack Schaefer and the American West** Jack Schaefer
**Goalkeepers are Crazy** Brian Gianville
**A James Joyce Selection** James Joyce
**Out of the Air** Five radio plays, *edited by* Alfred Bradley
**Could it be?** *edited by* Michael Marland
**The Minority Experience** *edited by* Michael Marland *and* Sarah Ray
**Scene Scripts Two** Five television plays
**Caribbean Stories** *edited by* Michael Marland
**An Isherwood Selection** *edited by* Geoffrey Halson
**A Thomas Hardy Selection** *edited by* Geoffrey Halson
**While They Fought** *edited by* Michael Marland *and* Robin Willcox
**The Wave and other stories** Liam O'Flaherty
**Irish Short Stories** *edited by* Frances Crowe
**The Experience of Parenthood** *edited by* Chris Buckton
**The Experience of Love** *edited by* Michael Marland
**A D.H. Lawrence Selection** *edited by* Geoffrey Halson

*Cassette available